# Streamline ENGLISH

PETER VINEY

## DIRECTIONS

**WORKBOOK B**
**UNITS 31–60**

Oxford University Press

Oxford University Press
Great Clarendon Street, Oxford OX2 6DP

Oxford  New York
Athens  Auckland  Bangkok  Bogota
Bombay  Buenos Aires  Calcutta  Cape Town
Dar es Salaam  Delhi  Florence  Hong Kong
Istanbul  Karachi  Kuala Lumpur  Madras
Madrid  Melbourne  Mexico City  Nairobi
Paris  Singapore  Taipei  Tokyo  Toronto

and associated companies in
Berlin  Ibadan

*Oxford* and *Oxford English* are trade marks
of Oxford University Press

ISBN 0 19 432239 4 (workbook A)
ISBN 0 19 432240 8 (workbook B)
ISBN 0 19 432272 6 (student's edition)
ISBN 0 19 432273 4 (teacher's edition)
ISBN 0 19 432274 2 (set of 2 cassettes)

**Acknowledgements**

*Illustrations by:*
Edward McLachlan
Peter Dennis

*Photographs by:*
Rob Judges

The publishers and author would like
to thank all the copyright holders for
their permission to reproduce the
extracts in this book:

*Unreliable memoirs* by Clive James,
Jonathan Cape Ltd, A. D. Peters and
Co Ltd; *100 missing after Nile steamer
sinks* Daily Express; *300 die on Nile,
Hunt for baby in a dustcart* Daily Mail;
*'47 dead' as fire sinks ferry* Reuters Ltd;
*Computer age* by Dawn Gordon,
Rolling Stone (January 20, 1983); *'Blue
Code' for Water Safety* The Royal Life
Saving Society UK; *Death on the Nile
for 47* The Sun.

The publishers would like to thank
the following for permission to use
photographs:

British Tourist Authority
Camera Press Ltd
Minolta (UK) Ltd
Sunday Magazine/Colorific!
The J Allan Cash Photo Library

Filmset in Palatino by
Filmtype Services Limited,
Scarborough, North Yorkshire.

Printed in Hong Kong.

# To The Teacher

*Workbook B* of *Streamline English Directions* consists of thirty units. Each unit relates directly to the equivalent units in *Streamline English Directions* Student's Book, Units 31–60.

The *Workbook* provides additional written exercises, together with a comprehensive and graded approach to two- and three-word verbs, and word building. It should be used after the corresponding units in the Student's Book. It may be used in the following ways:

1 As additional classroom material, providing extra oral practice, written reinforcement and consolidation of the core material in the Student's Book. It provides longer written exercises, both guided and free. Short notes on the content and ways of exploitation can be found in the *Teacher's Edition* of *Streamline English Directions*.

2 On short intensive courses it can be used for homework outside the classroom.

3 It can also be used as an independent supplementary course for written reinforcement, and work on two-word verbs and word building with other courses at the level.

Features of the *Workbook* include:

1 Authentic texts with exercises designed to develop the reading skill.

2 Extracts from reference materials which will help the students to become accustomed to working alone with dictionaries and grammar books.

3 Exercises designed to stimulate the students' ability to write longer passages, both guided and free.

4 Material which can be used for oral work in pairs and groups.

5 Graded exercises on two-word verbs and word building.

6 Exercises on punctuation.

*Workbook A* is also available for Units 1–30 of the Student's Book.

*Acknowledgements*
I would like to thank Karen Viney for her ideas and comments on the materials. *Peter Viney*

# Unit 31

## 300 die on Nile

### Blazing steamer sinks in lake full of crocodiles

ABOUT 300 people were missing and believed to be dead after a steamer caught fire and sank in a crocodile-infested lake on the Nile yesterday.

Police said 48 bodies had been recovered. But 310 people had been saved — plucked from the dangerous waters after leaping from the blazing ship.

One man was pulled safely ashore — only to be bitten by one of the many scorpions that swarm along the banks. His condition became critical.

The disaster happened on the world's biggest man-made lake, Lake Nasser, behind Egypt's Aswan High Dam near the border with Sudan.

The aging Egyptian steamer, The 10th of Ramadan, set out on Monday afternoon for a routine 48-hour voyage from Aswan in Egypt to Wadi Halfa in Sudan.

The passengers were mainly poor people who could not afford to travel by air. There were 599 passengers — 547 Sudanese, 48 Egyptians, one Frenchman, one New Zealander, one Tanzanian and one person from Chad — and 28 Egyptian crew.

It was night and the ship was a few miles from the famed temples of Abu Simbel when a gas bottle apparently exploded, setting fire to the engine room.

The blaze spread and the completely gutted vessel sank.

The lake at that point is 180–240 feet deep and 12 miles wide, and full of crocodiles. But the desperate passengers hurled themselves into the water to escape burning to death.

Several were rescued by fishermen. Others swam ashore or to small islands and were picked up by four helicopters sent by the air force.

Fifty frogmen and rescue workers were flown to the area as well as a team of doctors and 20 tons of medicine.

The Ministers of Tourism, Tewik Ismail, and Social Affairs, Mrs Amal Osman, also flew to the scene of the disaster to supervise the rescue operation.

Injured passengers were taken to hospitals in Abu Simbel and Aswan.

The disaster was the worst in the area since December 1976 when the Egyptian vessel Petro sank in the Red Sea and about 100 people drowned.

In 1981 the steamer Bardis capsized at Edfu, north of Aswan, and 13 out of 83 passengers died.

The 10th of Ramadan had been shuttling to and fro along the lake for the past 10 years.

*Daily Mail*

## 100 missing after Nile steamer sinks

More than 100 passengers were feared drowned when an Egyptian vessel sank in crocodile-infested waters.

The ageing Nile steamer carrying 599 passengers and 28 crew burned out completely and foundered in the world's largest man-made lake, the Dam lake, in Southern Egypt.

The ferry, the Tenth of Ramadan, which shuttles between Aswan in Southern Egypt, and Wadi Halfa, in Northern Sudan, sank about 170 miles south of Aswan at dawn on Wednesday.

The Middle East News Agency said 183 people were saved and seven bodies had been recovered. But it quoted Aswan police chief as saying that 50 had been rescued.

The lake, behind the Aswan Dam, is 12 miles wide and more than 200ft deep.

Most of the passengers on the vessel, which has been ferrying on the same route for 10 years, were Sudanese. The crew were Egyptian.

The accident was the worst since 1976 when the Egyptian vessel Petra sank in the Red Sea and about 100 people drowned.

About 50 rescue workers and frogmen were flown to the area and four reconnaissance planes were sent to help.

One rescued passenger was said to have been stung by a scorpion after he was saved and was said to be "critical".

*Daily Express*

## '47 dead' as fire sinks ferry

A ferry-boat crossing from Egypt to Sudan with more than 600 passengers and crew caught fire and sank early yesterday close to the pharaonic temples of Abu Simbel on Lake Nasser.

Full details of casualties were still not known last night in Cairo, but 500 people had been rescued and there were suggestions that 47 bodies had been recovered. Nearly all the passengers were Sudanese. Reports that more than 100 people had lost their lives in the crocodile-infested waters could not be confirmed.

A rescue operation including four army helicopters, four police river boats and frogmen, was launched from Aswan, 200 miles north of Abu Simbel, to look for survivors in the crocodile-infested waters of the lake.

The ship, Ramadan 10, owned by a Sudanese-Egyptian joint venture company, "disintegrated and sank" according to the Egyptian official news agency. Causes of the fire were not given.

Ferries between Egypt and Sudan are always very crowded. As there is no road linking the two countries, the ferry is the only overland route.

Unconfirmed reports suggested that the explosion of a gas cylinder in the kitchens of the ship could have set off the fire.

Ferries crossing the man-made stretches of Lake Nasser usually moor for the night about 100 yards from the shore, close to Abu Simbel.

Apart from its Sudanese passengers, the ship was carrying 48 Egyptians and four others, including one Frenchman.

The ferry disaster coincided with the first session of the joint Egyptian-Sudanese Nile Valley Parliament, held yesterday in the Sudanese capital.

*The Guardian*

## Death on the Nile for 47

AT LEAST 47 people were drowned yesterday when a crowded Nile steamer caught fire and sank in crocodile-infested waters.

The ferry, with 600 Sudanese on board, was steaming from Egypt to Sudan when the blaze started in the engine room.

Hundreds of people were pulled from the river by rescuers.

*The Sun*

|  | Daily Mail | Daily Express | The Sun | The Guardian |
|---|---|---|---|---|
| Number on boat |  |  |  |  |
| Passengers |  |  |  |  |
| Crew |  |  |  |  |
| Number dead |  |  |  |  |
| Number saved |  |  |  |  |
| Bodies actually recovered |  |  |  |  |
| Missing, believed dead |  |  |  |  |
| Distance from Abu Simbel |  |  |  |  |
| Cause of fire |  |  |  |  |

## Exercise 1

Read all the newspaper reports from Thursday 26th May 1983 and complete the table above. Put X if no information is given.

## Exercise 2

1 Which report is the most interesting to read?
2 Which do you think is the most accurate?
3 Why do you think there are differences?

## Word study

### Nouns ending in '-ability' and '-ibility'

probable  *probability*
visible  *visibility*

**Note:** adjectives ending in '-able' and '-ible' form nouns ending in '-ability' and '-ibility'.

## Exercise 3

Form nouns from these adjectives.

1 possible............................
2 legible..............................
3 able..................................
4 respectable.......................
5 capable............................
6 audible.............................
7 credible............................
8 desirable...........................
9 flexible.............................
10 impossible.......................

## Two-word verbs: catch and drop

*catch on*  become popular
*catch on*  understand
*catch out*  detect someone in a lie or a crime
*catch up*  come up to a person going in the same direction
*catch up (on)* ⎫
*catch up with* ⎭ do something that needs to be done

*drop away/off*  fall to nothing (especially statistics)
*drop back/behind*  go slower, so as to be behind
*drop in/by*  visit casually
*drop out*  stop trying/competing

## Exercise 4

Complete the sentences with 'catch' or 'drop'.

1 Home computers have ....... on very quickly.
2 I ....... in at John's house for tea.
3 It sold well for a few months, then sales ....... away to almost nothing.
4 What? Sorry? Perhaps I'm a bit slow to ....... on, but I don't know what you mean.
5 'Silver Prince' led the race for the first mile, then ....... back into second place.
6 He told everyone his father was a lord, but he was ....... out when his father, who was a bank clerk, visited him.
7 I'm so tired. I've had several late nights. I need to ....... up on sleep.
8 She had two university degrees, but she ....... out and took a job as a bus conductor.

# Unit 32

## Language summary

### Punctuation: the comma

Commas are used:

- to separate items in a list
  *Before the holiday she bought soap, shampoo, toothpaste, a new toothbrush and a toilet bag.*

  **Note:** you do not need a comma before 'and'.

- to separate phrases
  *I often spend the evenings watching television, writing letters, reading books and phoning friends.*

- before and after anything that interrupts the sentence
  *The news, although I had been expecting it, gave me a shock.*

- before and after a part of the sentence which gives more information about the subject
  *Johnny Rabid, who is the lead vocalist of The Rats, was interviewed on the Parkhurst Show last night.*

- after adverbial phrases and clauses, and phrases without a verb that come before the main verb
  *When the sun shines, everyone's in a better mood.*
  *Exhausted by the day, she fell asleep.*

- to separate main clauses joined by a conjunction
  *I'd always wanted to meet him, but was disappointed when I did.*

- after words like 'yes', 'no' and 'thank you'
  *No, I don't agree.*
  *Yes, I do.*
  *Thank you, but I'll be busy.*

- before tag questions
  *It's a nice day, isn't it?*
  *He doesn't like it, does he?*

- to break up numbers into groups
  *1,520,254   2,175   100,000   10,000*

  **Note:** don't use commas for dates (1986) or for decimals (3.5   98.4   1.25).

- in direct speech
  *'I love you,' he said. 'You're the only one for me.'*
  *'I,' he said, 'am Sir John.'*

- after names or short phrases at the beginning of sentences
  *Chloe, are you ready for dinner yet?*

- after adverbs, and words like 'however' and 'nevertheless' at the start of a sentence
  *Surprisingly, he failed his driving test.*
  *However, I'm sure he'll pass next time.*

---

## Exercise 1

There are often misprints in newspapers. Here are a few real examples.

1 Underline the misprint.
2 Replace it with the correct word.

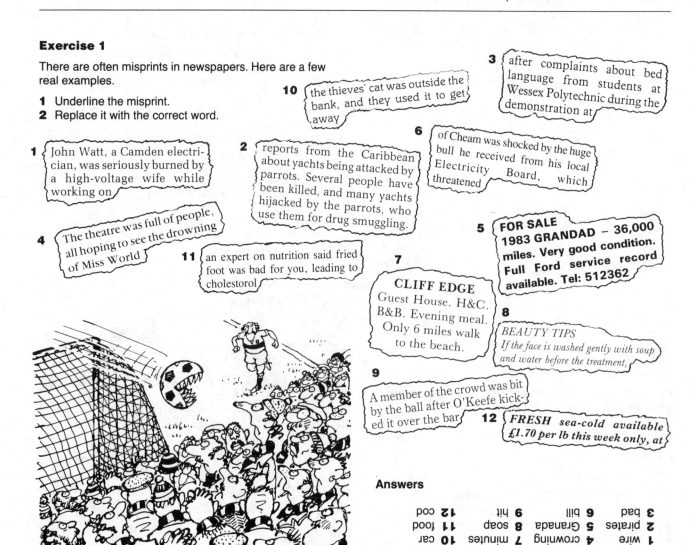

1 John Watt, a Camden electrician, was seriously burned by a high-voltage wife while working on

2 reports from the Caribbean about yachts being attacked by parrots. Several people have been killed, and many yachts hijacked by the parrots, who use them for drug smuggling.

3 after complaints about bed language from students at Wessex Polytechnic during the demonstration at

4 The theatre was full of people, all hoping to see the drowning of Miss World

5 FOR SALE
1983 GRANDAD – 36,000 miles. Very good condition. Full Ford service record available. Tel: 512362

6 of Cheam was shocked by the huge bull he received from his local Electricity Board, which threatened

7 **CLIFF EDGE**
Guest House. H&C. B&B. Evening meal. Only 6 miles walk to the beach.

8 *BEAUTY TIPS*
*If the face is washed gently with soup and water before the treatment,*

9 A member of the crowd was bit by the ball after O'Keefe kicked it over the bar

10 the thieves' cat was outside the bank, and they used it to get away

11 an expert on nutrition said fried foot was bad for you, leading to cholestorol

12 *FRESH sea-cold available £1.70 per lb this week only, at*

**Answers**

1 wife    4 crowning    7 minutes    10 car
2 pirates    5 Granada    8 soap    11 food
3 bad    6 bill    9 hit    12 cod

## Exercise 2

Put commas into these sentences where necessary.

1 The men who all came from England wore formal jackets white shirts black shoes and bow ties although it was a very hot evening.
2 'No I've never met him' he said. 'But he works in the same company doesn't he?' she replied.
3 'Thank you that's just what I want' she said. 'And I'd also like some cheese a packet of biscuits 250 grams of butter and a bottle of wine.'
4 'John can you help me for a moment?' she asked. 'You're not too busy are you?'
5 'Abbey Road' which was the Beatles' best-selling record sold millions of copies.
6 His car which he bought ten years ago has done nearly 250000 kilometres.
7 The best meal in the restaurant fillet steak in cream sauce is also the most expensive.
8 She's very fond of swimming lying on the beach water-skiing reading books and sunbathing.
9 Kathleen had always hoped to visit Ireland but had never had the time for a holiday.
10 'When he gets here ask him to come up to my office right away' said Mr Hunter. 'I want to question him about this £10000 contract he's been talking about.'

## Word study

### Nouns and adjectives ending in '-ist', '-ism' and '-ive'

-ist   *socialist, racist, Marxist, monarchist, Gaullist*
-ism  *socialism, racism, Marxism, monarchism, Gaullism*
-ive  *manipulative, supportive, preventive, assertive*

**Note:** words ending in '-ist' can be adjectives or nouns, words ending in '-ism' are usually nouns and words ending in '-ive' are usually adjectives.

## Exercise 3

Write down what these people believe in or follow.

1 a communist....................
2 a pacifist.......................
3 a socialist......................
4 a Leninist......................
5 a Stalinist......................

6 a monetarist.................
7 a Marxist......................
8 a fascist.......................
9 a Maoist......................
10 a Buddhist..................

## Exercise 4

Make adjectives from these verbs.

1 prevent...........................
2 suggest...........................
3 manipulate......................

4 support...........................
5 assert.............................
6 depress...........................

## Exercise 5

Use the dictionary extracts to complete these sentences.

1 The evenings are drawing .... . You can feel that winter's coming.
2 It was a terrible fight; this huge man started laying ... a much smaller one.
3 They had to lay ... two thousand men while the steel mill was being repaired.
4 A car drew ... and the driver asked us the way to the station.
5 Alberti, in the Ferrari, drew ... from the other cars at the beginning of the last lap.
6 Oh, come on. It isn't that good, you're laying ... ... a bit thick.
7 We've laid ... plenty of wine for the party.
8 It's been a bad year financially. We've had to draw ... our savings.
9 I like the plan. You've ... out all the possibilities very clearly.
10 They've ... up a new contract.

### Two-word verbs: draw and lay

**17** (uses with *adverbial particles* and *prepositions*):
**draw away,** go ahead of: *The horse quickly drew away from the others.*
**draw back,** (**a**) move away from: *He drew back in horror from the accident.* (**b**) (*fig*) show unwillingness: *∼ back from a proposal.* ⇨ drawback.
**draw in,** (**a**) (of a particular day) reach its end. (**b**) (of daylight) become shorter: *the days begin to ∼ in after midsummer.*
**draw on,** take or use as a source: *Journalists sometimes ∼ on their imaginations for stories. We mustn't ∼ on our savings.*
**draw out,** (**a**) (of days) become longer: *After Christmas the days began to ∼ out.* (**b**) persuade (a person) to talk, show feelings: *He has many interesting stories if you can ∼ him out.* (**c**) (cause to) become longer: *a 'long-∼-out discussion.*
**draw up,** (**a**) write out: *∼ up a contract.* (**b**) (cause to) come near to: *The taxi drew up at the station.* (**c**) **draw oneself up,** stand up straight: *He drew himself up to his full height.*

**11** (uses with *adverbial particles* and *prepositions*):
**lay sth aside,** (**a**) save; keep for future use: *∼ aside money for one's old age.* (**b**) put down: *He laid his book aside to listen to me.*
**lay sth by,** = lay sth aside(a).
**lay sb/oneself down,** place in a lying position. **lay sth down,** (**a**) pay or wager: *How much are you ready to ∼ down?* (**b**) (begin to) build: *∼ down a new ship.* (**c**) convert (land) to pasture: *∼ down land to grass.* (**d**) store (wine) in a cellar: *∼ down claret and port.* **lay down one's arms,** put one's weapons down as a sign of surrender. **lay down the law,** ⇨ law(2). **lay down one's life,** sacrifice it: *He laid down his life for his country.*
**lay sth in,** provide oneself with a stock of: *∼ in provisions/stores.*
**lay into sb,** (**a**) assault, attack. (**b**) criticize.
**lay off,** (*informal*) (**a**) discontinue: *The doctor told me to ∼ off work for a week.* (**b**) stop doing something which annoys: *You've been seeing my sister again—Well, you can just ∼*

*off.* **lay sb off,** dismiss (from work) temporarily: *∼ off workmen,* eg because of a shortage of materials. Hence, **'lay-off** *n* [C] period during which men are laid off.
**lay sth on,** (**a**) supply services to a building: *Are gas and water laid on?* (**b**) (*informal*) provide: *A party was laid on for the visitors.* **lay it on (thick/with a trowel),** use exaggerated praise, flattery, etc.
**lay sth out,** (**a**) spread out ready for use or so as to be seen easily: *∼ out one's evening clothes.* (**b**) prepare for burial: *∼ out a corpse.* (**c**) spend (money): *∼ out on a new suit.* (**d**) make a plan for; arrange well: *well laid-out streets and avenues.* Hence, **'lay-out** *n* [C] arrangement, plan, of a printed page, a factory etc.
**lay sth up,** (**a**) save; store: *∼ up provisions.* (**b**) ensure by what one does or fails to do that one will have trouble, etc in future: *∼ing up trouble for yourself.* (**c**) put (a ship) out of commission: *∼ a ship up for repairs.* **be laid up,** forced to stay in bed: *He's laid up with a broken leg.*

# Unit 33

## Language summary

See Student's Book

Titan rocket at Cape Kennedy

US Gemini capsule

### Exercise 1

Look at the Language Study in the Student's Book. Now read this extract from Rick van Haskins' book, *Descendants of the Astronauts?* (Feeble and Fable) page 387. Underline the expressions which indicate belief and certainty.

It was on my first visit to the step pyramid of Natzu-Lupu that I became absolutely convinced that our ancestors were visitors from outer space. The pyramid lies deep in the jungle regions between Ecuador and Peru, and few people have ever heard of it. Archaeologists believe it to be an Inca temple, but without doubt the building is much more than that. It is obvious that the pyramid was designed to enable astronauts to enter a space vehicle. The circular area directly to the south of the pyramid is clearly the launching pad, which was paved with stone blocks. I have no doubts that the stone blocks were put together by an alien society. There is no question that the stone comes from the mountains 100 miles away. It would have been impossible for the people of the time to have moved the blocks so far, or to have fitted them together so accurately. The centre of the circle is blackened and burnt, no doubt by the exhaust vapours from the space craft's departure – just compare the pyramid to the picture of a Titan rocket. If any further proof is necessary, it can be found in a wall painting which I discovered inside the pyramid. It is my sincere belief that this painting portrays an astronaut inside a space capsule. Look again at the picture of a Gemini space capsule. We can clearly see the space helmet, with its transparent visor and the radio antennae on top. The machinery on the astronaut's chest might have been controls, or even breathing apparatus. Natzu-Lupu proves my theories. Not even my most cynical critics can dispute the evidence.

### Exercise 2

Look again at the Language study in the Student's Book. Then read Professor Tom Katz's review of *Descendants of the Astronauts?* Underline the expressions of disbelief.

I've always mistrusted van Haskins' conclusions, but in this new book he is really absurd. Take the story about Natzu-Lupu. I don't know anyone who has ever heard of it, and I doubt whether there is such a place. Anyway, just think about it. I doubt whether a society which could build spaceships would need gigantic steps to get into them! Van Haskin compares it with a Titan rocket. Can you really imagine that an advanced interplanetary civilization would use 1962-style booster rockets? There are many step pyramids in the area, and they are quite simply Inca temples. The Incas were quite able to fit stones together accurately. As for the blackened area in the centre, I have no doubt that the colour was caused by ordinary fires over a number of years. The wall painting is claimed to show an astronaut with a helmet. As a matter of fact, it's just a picture of a man. I can't see a helmet. It's obviously the man's hair style. I'm quite sure the objects on the head are decorative feathers, and that we can see typical Inca body armour on his chest. It's just a picture of a man sitting down. I must admit that the book is an entertaining read but is it fact? Well, I've put my copy in the fiction section of my bookshelf.

### Exercise 3

Look through the two passages again.
Think of other stories about visitors from space that you have heard. Do you believe or dispute them? Why/why not? Write a paragraph expressing your own opinion of the wall painting and the pyramid of Natzu-Lupu.

## Exercise 4

Either act out an argument between van Haskins and Katz on a TV programme, or write it out in the form of a dialogue.

## Exercise 5

Write sentences expressing your belief, doubt, disbelief, or uncertainty about the statements below.

1 Whisky's the best treatment for a cold.
2 The shroud of Jesus is in Turin cathedral.
3 Earth has been visited by aliens.
4 A pink sky at night is a sign of good weather.
5 Some ancient monuments were left by alien astronauts.
6 Man has evolved from lower animals.
7 Neil Armstrong walked on the moon.
8 A nuclear war would totally destroy the world.
9 My country is the best place in the world.
10 Two and two make four.

## Word study

### Nouns ending in '-or', '-our' and '-ure'

-or     agent nouns usually use the '-or' ending:
*actor, doctor, food processor*

-our    abstract nouns usually use the '-our' ending:
*honour, labour, behaviour, humour, glamour, flavour*

Important exceptions (abstract nouns with '-or') are
*error, horror, terror, tremor*

**Note:** in American English, '-our' nearly always becomes '-or'.

-ure    *nature, measure, closure, temperature, adventure, pleasure, pressure, treasure, gesture, leisure*

## Exercise 6

List the words in the two extracts (Exercises 1 and 2) ending in '-or', '-our' and '-ure'.

## Exercise 7

Complete the sentences using the Word study and the list you have just made.

1 British Airways announce the ....... of flight BA 172 to Madrid.
2 He likes to watch ....... films, like *Dracula,* in his ....... time.
3 The Earth ....... shook the house. We felt real ....... to experience the power of ....... at such close quarters.
4 The isobar is a ....... of barometric ........
5 I like ....... stories, you know, ones about pirate ....... and desert islands.
6 Oh, pink ice-cream! I hate the ......., but when I eat it, I like the strawberry ........

### Two-word verbs: A–E

| | | | |
|---|---|---|---|
| *add up* | *blow out* | *brush up* | *close down* |
| *ask out* | *blow up* | *build up* | *dress up* |
| *beat up* | *book up* | *clear up* | *end up* |

**Note:** this is not a complete list of two-word verbs A–E.

## Exercise 8

Match the sentences in Column A with the explanations in Column B, by writing the number of the sentence in the appropriate boxes.

| | Column A | Column B |
|---|---|---|
| 1 | I asked her out. | It punctured and burst. |
| 2 | I'll clear up. | He's gradually developed it. |
| 3 | It doesn't add up. | You should reserve seats in advance. |
| 4 | The bomb blew up. | The figures are not correct *or* I don't understand it. |
| 5 | Children love dressing up. | There's a mess. I'll tidy the mess. |
| 6 | Someone beat him up. He was in hospital for 2 days. | The result of his behaviour will one day be prison. |
| 7 | He'll end up in prison. | He was hit, kicked and punched badly. |
| 8 | I'm trying to brush up my German. | They like putting on different clothes and costumes. |
| 9 | It's closed down. | I invited her to go out with me. |
| 10 | My tyre suddenly blew out at 75 mph! | It exploded. |
| 11 | He's built up a good business. | I wish to improve my German. |
| 12 | His concerts are very popular. You'll have to book up. | It's closed, completely and permanently. |

# Unit 34

## Language summary

### Past habits

*I used to do it.*
*I didn't use to do it./I never used to do it.*
*Did you use to do it?*

### Present habits

*I'm used to doing this.*
*I'm not used to doing this.*
*I can't get used to doing that.*

### Verbs and -ing forms

(see Student's Book)

## Exercise 1

Carole Singer has become famous during the last three years. She's still only twenty-three and she owns her own private plane. She's made a fortune from computer programs which she started designing when she left school. Read her school report from seven years ago.

*She never used to work seriously in Social Studies.*
Write eight more sentences about Carole with 'used to'.

---

# REPORT

## Watermouth Comprehensive School

Name .....Singer................... First name .....Carole...........

Class ..5C.... Number in class ..32.... Position in class ...29....

| | | |
|---|---|---|
| English | D | Carole doesn't pay enough attention. She never hands in her homework. |
| Maths | A | Brilliant. Carole is exceptionally gifted and top of the class. |
| Social Studies | E | Carole is very childish. She needs to grow up and work more seriously. |
| French | E | Written and aural work very poor. Her accent is terrible and she doesn't try to improve it. |
| Physics | D | Carole never completes her work – a pity because she's not without talent. |
| Domestic Science | E | Her obvious boredom with Domestic Science disrupts the class. |
| P.E. | D | Carole tries to avoid any activity. She is very lazy. |
| Music | B | She enjoys music, is a good pianist and works hard - a pleasure to teach. |

Head Teacher's report  Carole has missed out on school a lot this year because of illness, but when she is here, she does as little as possible. She must realise the importance of her education and try harder in future.

E. G. Bennett
E.G. Bennett

## Exercise 2

If you're at school, think about your reports of three or four years ago. If you've left, think about your old school reports. Write eight sentences about yourself with 'used to'.

## Exercise 3

Think back to three or four years ago, or to the time you were at school. What did you use to be good or bad at doing? What did you use to be best at? What did you use to enjoy/dislike doing?

Write a paragraph commenting on your performance at school.

## Exercise 4

Rupert Smythe used to be one of the best-known playboys in London's West End. Three months ago he became fed up with his life, moved to the country and got a job as a gardener. His routine has certainly changed! As he says, he isn't used to doing manual work, but he's enjoying it and he's slowly getting used to it.

Use the information below to write six sentences with 'used to do', six with 'be used to doing' and six with 'get used to doing'.

OLD HABITS
Get up at 11.00/champagne breakfast/lunch 1.00 to 3.00/ tennis 4.30/evening — gambling, dancing, drinking to the early hours/always felt tired and bored.

NEW HABITS
Get up at 5.30/work 6.00 to 4.00/bread and cheese for lunch/lots of exercise/evening — simple meal at 6.00/pub 8.00 to 9.30/bed 10.00/always feels healthy and alive.

## Exercise 5

Look at the Language study in the Student's Book. Complete these sentences with the infinitive ('to do') or the '-ing' form ('doing').

1 I always get annoyed about people ....... in crowded places. (smoke)
2 I'm fed up with ....... here. (live)
3 I'll try ....... it before I go home. (finish)
4 I can't get used to ....... the one-pound coins. (use)
5 I intend ....... my aunt on Saturday. (visit)
6 Did you remember ....... the door? (lock) I know I didn't do it.
7 He's absolutely scared stiff of ........ . (fly)
8 It's a great book. I've just started ....... it. (read)
9 I was interested ....... your news. (hear)
10 I can't bear ....... early. (get up)

## Word study

### Nouns ending in '-hood', '-dom' and '-ship'

-hood means 'the state of being (something)', and is added to nouns *neighbourhood, motherhood, manhood, priesthood, nationhood*

-dom can be added to nouns
*kingdom, stardom, officialdom, serfdom, earldom*
and adjectives
*wisdom* (from wise), *freedom* (free), *boredom* (bored)

-ship can also mean 'the state of being (something)'
*friendship, relationship, ownership, censorship, sportsmanship*
and has an additional meaning of 'having skill in'
*workmanship, musicianship, scholarship*
You can also win a *scholarship* to a university (your fees will be paid), gain a *fellowship* there (an honorary title) and one day be appointed to a *professorship*.

## Exercise 6

Make abstract nouns from these nouns by adding '-hood'.
1 father..............................   5 widow..............................
2 boy..................................   6 parent.............................
3 mother.............................   7 brother............................
4 child................................   8 knight.............................

## Exercise 7

Fill in the spaces with words ending in '-ship'.

1 What a beautiful chair! It's 18th century and you can see how good the ....... was in those days.
2 After the goalkeeper came round, he got up and shook hands with the forward who had knocked him out. The crowd applauded his ....... .
3 I've known him well for ten years, and I very much value his ....... .
4 Is she his aunt or his cousin? I'm not sure of their ....... .
5 It's mine, even though I can't prove my ....... of it.

## Exercise 8

Some words ending in '-dom' have been missed out of these sentences. Fill in each space with the appropriate word.

1 Michael Jackson achieved ....... at an early age.
2 The owl is famous for its ....... .
3 ....... among teenagers is the the reason for a lot of vandalism.
4 William Tell fought for ....... for Switzerland.
5 My passport says 'The United ....... of Great Britain and Northern Ireland'.

### Two-word verbs: F — M

| | | | |
|---|---|---|---|
| *(be) fed up* | *grow up* | *hang on* | *live in* |
| *fill in* | *hand in* | *last out* | *lock up* |
| *finish off* | *hand out* | *laugh off* | *miss out* |
| *follow up* | *hang about/around* | *live down* | *mix up* |

## Exercise 9

Read through the unit again. Underline all the verbs from the list above that you find. Read the instructions too.

## Exercise 10

Complete the sentences.

1 After their ship sank, they only had a little food, but they made it ....... out for 15 days.
2 The police caught him. I hope they ....... him up and throw away the key.
3 Someone's ....... off the milk! Now, I'll have to have black coffee.
4 It was a terrible scandal. It will take her years to ....... it down.
5 Mr Smith? He's in the other room. Just ....... on for a moment. I'll go and fetch him.
6 His job is to ....... up all phone enquiries with a letter and a catalogue.
7 'Excuse me. That's my case.' 'Oh, sorry, they must have got ....... up on the flight.'
8 There's nothing to do in the evenings for teenagers, except to ....... round on street corners.

# Unit 35

## Language summary

**Past perfect**
*He had stolen the car.*

**Past perfect passive**
*The car had been stolen.*

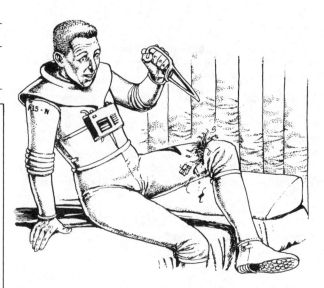

Jack laughed as he put down his cup. 'Well, tea-break over. We'd better get back to work.' Ben picked up his helmet and followed Jack to the door. They both walked into the air lock, closed the door and put on their helmets. Ben switched on his oxygen supply, then they opened the outer door and stepped out of the metal dome which had been their home for nearly ten years.

Ben looked up in disgust. As usual the purple-blue light from the twin suns reflected from the sharp rocks of the planetoid's surface. Methane vapour swirled up from the cracks between the rocks. Ten years! They had been put down onto the planetoid, which was called K14, by their starship ten years ago. K14 was a miserable, cold, empty satellite of the eleventh planet in the Gamma Shephard system, in one of the remotest corners of the galaxy.

Jack was walking slowly towards the huge machinery which was used for mining uranium. That was their job here. Their only excitement was the annual arrival of the starship, which collected the uranium, and left them the supplies they needed for survival. It was due in about fifteen earth-days from now. At least there would be new video tapes, perhaps some more computer games. Ben stood watching Jack as he approached the huge machine, which was throwing huge clouds of dust and rock upwards as it continued its automatic search for uranium. Both of them had been afraid of the machine when they arrived, but the fear had passed. Jack had stopped to look at something on the ground. Ben saw the machine as it moved and changed direction slightly. 'Jack!' he shouted into the intercom. 'Look out, it's . . .' He saw Jack begin to turn and look up, but it was too late. A huge rock seemed to come towards him in slow motion, it crashed into him, and Jack tumbled to the ground. Ben ran forwards. First he switched off the machine, then went to help Jack.

'Alone! I'm alone here,' was Ben's first thought as he looked at Jack's dead body. Jack was his best friend – no, his only friend. They had been here for such a long time together. Jack's neck had been broken by the rock. His spacesuit had been cut open. The poisonous atmosphere of K14 would have killed him if the rock hadn't already done so. Ben looked at Jack's neck in horror. It was cut, and through the cut he could see wires. He looked closely, yes . . . there were wires, printed circuits, electrical relays . . . solenoids.

Jack had been an android, a robot designed to look like a real human being. Ben sat back, and felt hot tears running down his face. 'My best friend was . . . was a robot,' he thought.

He staggered back to the dome. Once he was inside, he took off his helmet and turned to the main computer. 'Jack was a robot,' he said. 'Why? Why didn't you tell me?'

The soft, friendly voice of the computer replied, 'You needed company. You needed a friend.'

'But . . . why a robot?'

'You must understand, Ben. The working conditions here are very bad. It's difficult to find enough people who can put up with it, who can stick it out for ten or twenty years.'

'I'm going to my room,' Ben said.

Ben closed the door. It was true. They had been trying to make it easier for him. After all, who would work seven days a week, 365 days a year, without holidays, without seeing anyone, without any . . . without any payment?

Ben walked over to the shelf, and picked up a knife. He sat on the bed staring at his leg. He had to know. He lifted the knife and plunged it into his leg. He grimaced with the pain, and then began to laugh hysterically at the pattern of multi-coloured wires and printed circuits spilling out just above his knee.

## Exercise 1

Find words which are similar in meaning to these words or phrases.

1 like a planet
2 a robot like a human being
3 a coil of wire magnetized by an electrical current
4 a moon
5 a rounded roof with a circular base
6 a space vehicle able to fly between different star systems
7 a colourless inflammable gas
8 a two-way radio
9 fell
10 like a slowed down film
11 walked or moved unsteadily
12 pushed suddenly and with great force
13 made an ugly, twisted facial expression

## Exercise 2

Are these statements true or false? Tick the appropriate boxes.

| | True | False |
| --- | --- | --- |
| 1 K14 was a moon. | ☐ | ☐ |
| 2 They were the only occupants of K14. | ☐ | ☐ |
| 3 Jack was killed by methane gas. | ☐ | ☐ |
| 4 Ben had known that he was an android. | ☐ | ☐ |
| 5 Ben had never been paid. | ☐ | ☐ |
| 6 This story takes place in the distant future. | ☐ | ☐ |
| 7 The starship arrived once a month. | ☐ | ☐ |
| 8 The machine was automatic. | ☐ | ☐ |

## Exercise 3

Write full answers to these questions.

1 How long had they been living there?
2 When had they been put down there?
3 What was the machine used for doing?
4 What did the starship use to leave them?
5 Were they still afraid of the machine?
6 What had Jack stopped to do?
7 What did the machine do?
8 How had Jack been killed?
9 What had happened to his space suit?
10 What did Ben have to know?
11 How did he find the answer?

## Word study

### Nouns ending in '-al' and '-oid'

-al  *denial, refusal, proposal, withdrawal*

**Note:** nouns ending in '-al' are formed from verbs.

-oid  *spheroid, humanoid, cuboid, asteroid*

**Note:** nouns ending in '-oid' usually mean 'like' or 'resembling'. These nouns often appear in science-fiction stories and films.

*humanoid*  an inhabitant of another planet who looks human

*android*  a robot designed to look human

*hominoid*  man-like creatures on Earth (for example, the yeti or abominable snowman)

### Exercise 4

List all the nouns ending in '-al' and '-oid' in the story.

### Exercise 5

Form nouns from these verbs.

1 arrive
2 survive
3 deny
4 propose
5 refuse
6 withdraw
7 renew
8 reverse
9 dismiss
10 recite

### Exercise 6

Finish these sentences. Use a dictionary if necessary.

1 Something like a human is a ........ .
2 Something like a cube is a ........ .
3 Something like a planet is a ........ .
4 Something like a star (Latin: *astra*) is an ........ .

### Two-word verbs: O – S

| own up | play down | show off | slip up | split up |
| pay up | pop in | show up | speak out | stick out |
| pick up | rule out | shut up | speak up | sum up |

### Exercise 7

Match the sentences in Column A with the explanations in Column B. Write the number of each sentence in the appropriate box.

| | Column A | Column B |
|---|---|---|
| 1 | He's very modest. He's trying to play down his success. | Who did it? You'd better admit it! |
| 2 | If you don't agree you should speak out. | Redundancies are not impossible. |
| 3 | He went to the dance hoping to pick up a girl. | She wants everyone to admire her. |
| 4 | John and Mary have split up. | He summarised the major points of the argument. |
| 5 | Nobody showed up for the party. | Can you continue until it's over? |
| 6 | He summed up the argument. | Pay me what you owe me. |
| 7 | Pop in and see me when you have time. | They've stopped seeing each other. |
| 8 | I slipped up when I thought she was his daughter. | He doesn't want to exaggerate his success, quite the opposite in fact. |
| 9 | His teacher spoke up for him. | If you don't agree you should say so. |
| 10 | You own me £10. You'd better pay up! | I made a mistake. |
| 11 | Can you stick it out? | Be quiet! |
| 12 | She likes to show off. | Come and visit me. |
| 13 | Shut up! | His teacher defended him, and told them about his good qualities. |
| 14 | I can't rule out the possibility of redundancies. | Nobody came to the party. |
| 15 | Whoever did this had better own up. | He wanted to meet a girl and invite her out. |

# Unit 36

## Language summary

### Giving advice

*should/shouldn't*
*ought to/ought not to*
*had better/had better not*
*If I were you, I'd . . .*
*Why don't you . . .?/Why not . . .?*
*My advice/The best advice is to . . .*

### Exercise 1

Fill in the questionnaire below.

**Questionnaire: How healthy are your eating habits?**

1 Is your weight within five kilos of the average for your height?
Yes ☐ No ☐

2 Do you generally have two or three medium-sized meals a day rather than snacks and just one big meal?
Yes ☐ No ☐

3 Do you go to bed more than three hours after your main evening meal?
Yes ☐ No ☐

4 Do you have leisurely meals, instead of eating quickly while doing other things?
Yes ☐ No ☐

5 Do you have a proper breakfast, rather than a coffee and a roll?
Yes ☐ No ☐

6 Do you use oil for cooking, and low-fat margarine, rather than fat (lard) and butter?
Yes ☐ No ☐

7 Do you eat fewer than five portions of fried food a week?
Yes ☐ No ☐

8 Do you eat fewer than five eggs a week?
Yes ☐ No ☐

9 Do you drink less than half a litre of milk a day?
Yes ☐ No ☐

10 Do you eat at least two portions of high-fibre food (such as wholemeal bread, unpolished rice, fruit, leafy vegetables or beans) every day?
Yes ☐ No ☐

11 Do you often choose fish or white meat (such as chicken) rather than red, fatty meats like beef or lamb?
Yes ☐ No ☐

12 If you eat between meals, do you eat fresh fruit rather than sweets, cakes or biscuits?
Yes ☐ No ☐

13 Do you taste food before adding salt?
Yes ☐ No ☐

14 Do you drink tea or coffee without added sugar?
Yes ☐ No ☐

15 Do you avoid sweetened soft drinks and drink water or fresh fruit juice, instead?
Yes ☐ No ☐

16 Do you limit coffee and tea to four cups a day?
Yes ☐ No ☐

### Exercise 2

Go through the questionnaire and work out your score. If possible, ask another student the questions, and work out his or her score.

### Score

12–16 'Yes' answers: you have a healthy diet.
9–12 'Yes' answers: your diet could be improved.
0–8 'Yes' answers: your diet should be improved.

### Exercise 3

1 According to the questionnaire, too much of some of these things are bad for you. Underline them.

| | | |
|---|---|---|
| salt | sweetened soft drinks | chicken |
| milk | eggs | butter |
| unpolished rice | biscuits | beans |
| fried food | beef | white fish |
| low-fat margarine | leafy vegetables | red meats |
| lamb | beans | fruit |
| lard | wholemeal bread | |
| fish | coffee | |
| tea | cakes | |

2 Do you agree that you shouldn't eat the foods that are bad for you? Why/Why not?
Write out your views in note form.

## Exercise 4

Read through the questionnaire again. Write sixteen pieces of advice for someone who has sixteen 'No' answers. Try and vary the way you do this. Use the Language summary to help you.

## Exercise 5

1 Why are these things supposed to be harmful? Either ask some other students or write some possible reasons.
2 What illnesses are they supposed to lead to? If you don't know, try to find out. Write a paragraph based on your results.

## Exercise 6

1 Cholesterol, sugar, salt and some food colourings and preservatives are supposed to be bad for you. Which foods contain them? Make a list.
2 Read the two quotes below. Look at the notes you made in Exercise 3. Write a short paragraph stating your reactions to the quotes and your views.

*Eat what you like and let the food fight it out inside you.* (Mark Twain)

*You are what you eat. A healthy diet is most important.* (Anonymous)

## Word study

### Professions and roles ending with '-ian', '-ant', and '-ent'

-ian *musician, politician, mathematician, physician (=doctor), librarian, vegetarian, historian, magician*

**Note:** music *musician*. Generally '-ic(s)' becomes '-ician'.

-ant *accountant, assistant, attendant, consultant, immigrant*

-ent *president, superintendent, patient, resident*

## Exercise 7

Write down the noun for the person who practises, or works with the following.

1 music............................
2 libraries..........................
3 maths.............................
4 history............................
5 statistics.........................
6 magic.............................

## Exercise 8

*Someone who works with accounts is an accountant.*

Complete these sentences.

1 Someone who gives information is an ............................ .
2 Someone who inhabits a place is an ............................ .
3 Someone who makes a claim is a .................................. .
4 Someone with whom you correspond is a ..................... .
5 Someone who assists is an ........................... .
6 Someone you consult about something is a ................... .
7 Someone who resides somewhere is a ........................ .
8 Someone who superintends something is a .................. .

## Two-word verbs: T – W

*talk over*   discuss
*talk round*   persuade
*tell off*   criticize, blame
*think over* consider
*think up*   invent
*throw out*   reject
*try out*   test
*use up*   finish
*warm up*   reheat, prepare
*wear off*  gradually disappear

*wear out*   exhaust, finish
*weigh up*   consider two possibilities
*win over*   gain someone's support or agreement
*wind up*   bring to an end, make nervous
*write off*   damage beyond repair

**Note:** 'talk round' and 'win over' have very similar meanings.

## Exercise 9

Complete these sentences with words from the list above. Be careful of the tense.

1 Mike's very good at ....... ....... excuses when he's late for work. This morning he claimed he'd got his toe stuck in the bath tap!
2 Yes, it's a good idea. Can you let me ....... it ....... for a few days?
3 She'd drunk far too much. It was mid-morning before the hangover ....... ....... .
4 Look! I've only had these shoes for three months, and they've ....... ....... .
5 I've been ....... ....... this new washing powder, and everything is certainly much cleaner since I started using it.
6 'Hello. I won't be home till late.'
   'Oh, dear. Well, we'll have to ....... ....... your dinner when you get here.'
7 There's a terrible noise from the hi-fi next door. I can't think. It's beginning to ....... me ....... .
8 Coffee? Oh, don't open the new jar yet. Try and ....... ....... what's left in the old jar first.
9 They crashed the car into a tree and completely ....... it ....... .
10 The boss really ....... him ....... for telling stupid stories.
11 She won't speak to me since we had a row. I've been trying to ....... her ......., but she doesn't listen.
12 We could buy either of them. I'm trying to ....... ....... the possibilities.
13 'Look, another broken cup!'
    'Well don't ....... it ....... . Let me try to mend it.'
14 Pop in to see me about ten, and we'll ....... ....... the problem.

# Unit 37

## Language summary

### Relative clauses

*That's the place where it happened.*
*That's the thing which did it.*
*He's the person who did it.*
*That's the day when it happened.*
*She's the one whose husband was there.*

### Exercise 1

Mr Pearson and Miss Kent were involved in an accident. This is Mr Pearson's description of the accident. Complete the passage with 'who', 'which', 'where', 'when' or 'whose'.

I was driving along the High Street towards the multi-storey car park ....... I usually park my car. I was approaching the traffic lights ....... are on the corner of Oxford Avenue. The lights were green. The lights changed to red, and I braked. The Mini ....... was travelling behind me failed to stop and crashed into the rear of my car, ....... sustained damage to the bumper and rear lights. The girl ....... was driving the Mini got out, and was very rude and abusive. My wife ....... was in the front passenger seat of my car was very shaken and upset. The girl, ....... sister had been in the car with her, blamed us, and called us several rude names. I know it was exactly quarter past three ....... it happened because the clock in my car stopped.

### Exercise 2

This is the description of the accident Miss Kent sent to her insurance company. Complete the passage with 'who', 'which', 'where' or 'when'.

I was going along the High Street looking for a place ....... I could park. A big red Volvo was in front of me. The two people ....... were in the front seemed to be having an argument. I mentioned it to my sister, ....... was with me. The traffic lights, ....... had been green, changed to yellow. The Volvo was already half across them ....... it suddenly stopped. I had expected it to continue as the lights had only started to change, and I hit it. My car, ....... I had only had for two weeks, was a complete write-off. I got out. The woman, ....... husband had been driving, called me 'a young idiot'. They were both elderly. I suppose I was rude to them, too. It was about ten past three ....... the accident happened.

### Exercise 3

Write a paragraph saying whose fault you think the accident was and why.

### Exercise 4

Look at the accident report and the notes below. Write out two descriptions of the accidents, one for Mrs Bell and one for Mr Stavey. Use Exercises 1 and 2 as examples.

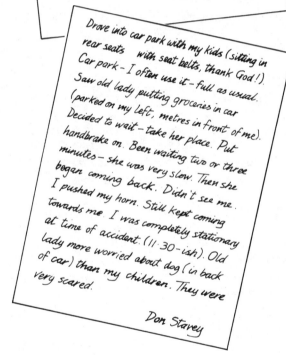

In underground car park behind supermarket. Always do shopping there. Happened 11·25 – looked at watch. Put shopping in car – next to dog (had left dog in car). Got in. Began to reverse from place I'd parked in. Sudden crash. Silver Sierra hit me. Must have come into car park quickly. Man driving car very angry. Nobody hurt. His children crying. Not my fault. His car damaged at front. Mine very bad. My dog ran away (I opened door). Haven't found it.

Angela Bell (Mrs)

Drove into car park with my kids (sitting in rear seats with seat belts, thank God!). Car park – I often use it – full as usual. Saw old lady putting groceries in car (parked on my left, metres in front of me). Decided to wait – take her place. Put handbrake on. Been waiting two or three minutes – she was very slow. Then she began coming back. Didn't see me. I pushed my horn. Still kept coming towards me. I was completely stationary at time of accident (11·30-ish). Old lady more worried about dog (in back of car) than my children. They were very scared.

Don Stavey

---

## CROWN MOTOR INSURANCE LTD
### Accident Report

Name ..ANGELA BELL (MRS)...................................... Vehicle registration ..KPV 114Y............................

Make...NISSAN........................ Model ..CHERRY............................ Year ..1983.................

Date and time of accident ...TUESDAY 9TH MARCH, 11:30 A.M..............

Location..WAITROSE CAR PARK, WINTON, BOURNEMOUTH..........................

Passengers.....1 (DOG)..................................................

**Details of other car(s):**

Name ..DON STAVEY.......................................... Vehicle registration ..A952 HPR............................

Make...FORD........................ Model ...SIERRA............................ Year ..1986..........................

Passengers..2 (CHILDREN).............................................

## Word study

### The order of adjectives

The usual order of adjectives is shown below. Use the table for reference only. In practice you hardly ever use all these types of adjectives at once.

| Quantity | Quality | Size | Shape | Age | Colour | | Pattern | Origin | Material | Object |
|---|---|---|---|---|---|---|---|---|---|---|
| How much/ many? | What's it like? | How big? | What shape? | How old? | What colour? | | What pattern? | Where's it from? | What's it made of? | What is it? |
| a(n) | ugly | little | flat | old | pale | red | striped | Chinese | wood | box |
| one | beautiful | medium- | round | modern | light | brown | plain | Greek | metal | table |
| five | cheap | sized | thin | 1984 | bright | green | check | Roman | leather | vase |
| some | clean | long | square | 1920s | dark | blue | spotted | Californian | plastic | shirt |
| a few | dirty | average- | oval | 15th | | black | flowered | European | aluminium | house |
| a lot of | nice | sized | pointed | century | | yellow | | Southern | cotton | |
| | | enormous | | antique | | | | | | |
| | | four- | | | | | | | | |
| | | seater | | | | | | | | |

### Exercise 5

*He washed a few, dirty, old, striped, cotton shirts.*

Write as many other reasonably logical sentences as you can using the words in the Word study.

### Exercise 6

She's got ............. dogs. (ugly, Pekinese, five, little)
*She's got five, ugly, little, Pekinese dogs.*

Rewrite these sentences, putting the adjectives in the most appropriate order.

1 He's just bought ............. car. (economical, Japanese, an, middle-sized)
2 My present was ............. . sweater. (blue, mohair, beautiful, a, light)
3 Can you give me ............. tomatoes? (Dutch, half a dozen, large)
4 It's ............. table. (18th century, little, a, mahogany, oval, lovely)
5 They live in ............. house. (1930s, four-bedroomed, brick, an, red, attractive)
6 I'm trying to find ............. system. (stereo, portable, Japanese, inexpensive, an)
7 She's wearing ............. dress. (cotton, pale, flowered, blue, a)
8 I'd like ............. grapes. (fresh, Italian, a bunch of, green)
9 There were ............. fans. (football, big, several, English, nasty, young, fat)
10 He's got ............. LPs. (rock, Californian, a lot of, southern)
11 She bought ............. plates. (plastic, bright, horrible, modern, eight, green, little)
12 She drives ............. car. (1920s, sports, two-seater, a, funny, little)

### Two-word verbs with 'away'

● Two-word verbs which consist of a verb of movement and an adverb usually have the literal meaning of the two parts, and are easy to understand! *Go away!*

● Sometimes it's not quite so easy, but it is still possible to guess: *he gave away a lot of money.* This is called a transferred meaning.

● Then there are the difficult ones, which can't be guessed from the meaning of the verb or adverb: *die away, work away.*

Two-word verbs with 'away' can be divided into four groups:

● **Literal meaning**
*be away, go away, keep away, stay away*

● **Transferred meaning**
*give away, put away, send/write away (for something), throw away*

● **Meaning 'getting less', 'disappearing'**
*The sound slowly died away.*
*It faded away to nothing.*
*The piece of wood had been eaten away by insects.*

● **Meaning 'without stopping'**
*They're working away at the job as hard as they can.*
*Fire away!* (Ask as many questions as you want)

### Exercise 7

Now complete the sentences. Be careful of the tense.

1 Yes, I saw the advertisement for the job. I've ....... away for an application form.
2 The last notes of the song ....... away, and the hall was silent. Then the audience began to applaud.
3 He had to ....... away from school for three weeks with measles.
4 The material had been ....... away by moths.
5 If you've got any queries, just ....... away, and I'll try to answer them.
6 He's been ....... away at his homework for two hours.
7 I won't need my heavy coat until the winter. I'll have it cleaned and ....... it away in the wardrobe.
8 ....... away from that wire! You'll get an electric shock.
9 I used to have a copy of that book, but I ....... it away to a friend.
10 I'm ....... away on holiday next week.

# Unit 38

They are charming but shallow.
They are not only charming but also generous.
Although they are generous they can also be greedy.

| They can be energetic. | In addition, | they can be persistent. |
| | Also, | |
| | Furthermore, | |

| Gemini people are | supposed | to be good businessmen. |
| | thought | |
| | said | |

---

# Signs of the Zodiac

**Aries**   The Ram   March 21–April 20

**Positive**
*strong, enthusiastic, positive, optimistic, ambitious*

**Negative**
*tactless, stubborn, unreasonable, irritable*

**Taurus**   The Bull   April 21–May 20

**Positive**
*honest, reliable, cautious, thorough*

**Negative**
*unforgiving, stubborn, materialistic, doesn't listen to others*

**Gemini**   The Twins   May 21–June 20

**Positive**
*bright, creative, charming, adaptable, intellectual*

**Negative**
*shallow, unreliable, doesn't concentrate, easily bored*

**Cancer**   The Crab   June 21–July 20

**Positive**
*home-loving, sympathetic, kind, loyal, patient*

**Negative**
*timid, unambitious, lazy, retiring*

**Leo**   The Lion   July 21–August 21

**Positive**
*leading, organizing, generous, hospitable, popular*

**Negative**
*arrogant, rude, conceited, materialistic*

**Virgo**   The Virgin   August 22–September 22

**Positive**
*hard-working, responsible, moderate, trustworthy, open*

**Negative**
*critical, cold, too tidy, miserly*

**Libra**   The Scales   September 23–October 22

**Positive**
*fair-minded, harmonious, considerate, artistic*

**Negative**
*insincere, escapist, vain, jealous*

**Scorpio**   The Scorpion   October 23–November 22

**Positive**
*brave, strong-willed, highly-principled, determined*

**Negative**
*boastful, sly, ruthless, vengeful*

**Sagittarius**   The Archer   November 23–December 20

**Positive**
*honest, broad-minded, practical, trusting*

**Negative**
*restless, risk-taking, tactless, undisciplined*

**Capricorn**   The Goat   December 21–January 19

**Positive**
*patient, serious, business-like, hard-working, self-controlled*

**Negative**
*bossy, narrow-minded, critical, materialistic*

**Aquarius**   The Water Carrier   January 20–February 18

**Positive**
*individualistic, honest, humanitarian*

**Negative**
*fanatical, eccentric, temperamental, impractical*

**Pisces**   The Fish   February 19–March 20

**Positive**
*idealistic, sympathetic, loving, trusting*

**Negative**
*depressive, gloomy, lazy, easily-led*

## Exercise 1

Make sentences about the signs of the Zodiac. Use each pattern from the Language summary twice.

## Exercise 2

Here are some descriptions of typical people for each of the signs. Use the chart (and your knowledge) to match the descriptions to the signs. The answers are upside down at the end of the unit.

1 They are happiest when they're at home. They are domesticated, cheerful, and affectionate. They are also sympathetic and sensitive. A kind, loyal friend.
2 They have hot tempers and biting tongues. They like giving orders. Furthermore, they are very strong-willed. They are good in emergencies. They make very bad enemies.
3 They are charming, intelligent and friendly, although I wouldn't trust them very much. They are creative and easy-going. They get fed up very quickly and also find it hard to concentrate for long.
4 Bold and daring, they are very ambitious. However, they are not only careless of others' feelings, but they are also poor listeners.
5 They are athletic and love outdoor life. In addition, they are very good with their hands. They don't mind hard work, but find it difficult to relax. They don't obey orders very well.
6 They are calm and hate quarrelling, perhaps they are unambitious. They made excellent parents and neighbours. On the negative side, they can be cool and mean with money.
7 They go from one extreme to the other. Life is a series of ups and downs. They care a lot for the problems of the world and major issues. They always stand out from the crowd. Not always very practical, though.
8 They are hard to understand. They are very easily influenced by others, and can be passive. They have strong family ties, but can be a little sad and unhappy.
9 They are fearless, although never foolishly so. They are trustworthy, and honest. They make friends and enemies easily, although they may not pay enough attention to others.
10 They are very just and believe in fairness. They always want good relations with everyone. They have excellent taste, and can also be artistic. They can be dreamers, and money slips through their fingers.
11 They are deep thinkers, often they are too serious. They make good students. Their temper can be sudden, and they like telling people what to do. They can also be intolerant, and sometimes moody.
12 Although jolly and cheerful, they can be impolite as well. They often make their way to the top. They think a lot of themselves, and though generous hosts, they are not one hundred per cent trustworthy.

## Exercise 3

Write a short paragraph saying how typical or untypical you are of your sign, or another student is of theirs.

## Exercise 4

Write your horoscope for tomorrow. Say what kind of day it will be for your star sign. Try and make it funny.

## Word study

### Review of adjectives

## Exercise 5

List the adjectives in 'Signs of the Zodiac' under these categories:

● words ending in '-ic', '-al', '-able', '-ian', '-y', '-ive', '-ful' or '-ing'
● compound words like 'open-minded' or 'round-shouldered'

## Exercise 6

Write the sign of the zodiac these adjectives apply to in the space provided.

| | | | |
|---|---|---|---|
| 1 | narrow-minded ............. | 9 | proud ........................... |
| 2 | sharp-tongued ................ | 10 | dreamy ......................... |
| 3 | quick-witted .................... | 11 | untrustworthy .............. |
| 4 | self-opinionated ............. | 12 | difficult ....................... |
| 5 | hypersensitive ................ | 13 | courageous ................. |
| 6 | good-humoured .............. | 14 | emotionless ................. |
| 7 | businesslike ................... | 15 | plain-spoken ............... |
| 8 | considerate .................... | 16 | emotional ..................... |

### Two-word verbs with 'back'

● **Literal meaning**
  **a** returning (to an earlier place or time)
  *be back, come back, get back, go back, send back, think back, turn back*
  **b** opposite of front
  *keep/stand stay back*
● **Transferred meaning**
  *give back, hand back, look back* (into the past), *put back, take back* (withdraw, apologize)
● **Return**
  *answer back* (defend oneself against criticism), *fight back, pay back* (have revenge), *pay back* (money)

## Exercise 7

Rewrite these sentences using two-word verbs from the list above.

1 I'll return here at 7 o'clock.
2 I'll repay you at the end of the month.
3 I often remember my first year away from home.
4 There was so much snow that we had to stop, turn round, and come home.
5 If they're going to attack us, we'll attack them.
6 The teachers never liked her because she always reacted angrily to any complaint or criticism.
7 If I upset you, I apologize for what I said.
8 In the autumn, the British move the hands on their clocks to one hour earlier.

### Answers to Exercise 2

| | | | | | |
|---|---|---|---|---|---|
| 1 | Cancer | 5 | Sagittarius | 9 | Taurus |
| 2 | Scorpio | 6 | Virgo | 10 | Libra |
| 3 | Gemini | 7 | Aquarius | 11 | Capricorn |
| 4 | Aries | 8 | Pisces | 12 | Leo |

# Unit 39

It's 6:22 p.m. as your car pulls into the driveway, the garage door silently ascends, and you roll inside. Stepping out of the car, you see the garage door descend. You pull out the familiar black card from your wallet and, as you insert the magnetic card into a slot by the door to your home, the lock clicks open, allowing you access. Once inside, you close the door, and the security system recycles for the next entry. As you pass from room to room on the way to the kitchen, the lights flick on around you, activated by the sound of your footsteps. You enter the kitchen to find your meal prepared and waiting; the microwave oven was activated an hour ago and has already reset itself for the next day. With tray in hand, you head for the den and settle down with your meal. The preprogrammed audio system switches on, playing your favorite record or tape.

At 7:12 p.m., tired and full, you place the dishes in the automatic dishwasher and head upstairs. A few minutes later, the downstairs lights switch off and the outside lights click on. It's been a long day, so you decide to relax in bed and watch reruns of *Battlestar Galactica*. And since you don't wish to be disturbed, your telephone answering machine intercepts all incoming calls.

By 12:24 a.m., you slip off to sleep. Moments later, the TV turns itself off, the lights dim, the thermostat lowers the temperature to fifty-nine degrees, and your alarm clock is set for 6:39 a.m. The house is quiet; all that can be heard is the sound of your breathing. But you are not alone – your house is awake, listening, feeling and waiting to start the coffee at 7:01 a.m.

The above scenario is no fantasy. With the help of a personal computer, most of this automation is possible. And if the idea of computers taking over your house makes you uneasy, you should realize that computers have already become part of our everyday lives. Automatic bank and telephone answering machines, pocket calculators and even microwave ovens use microprocessors very similar to those in computers.

The first modern computer was built in 1946. It was called ENIAC (Electronic Numerical Integrator and Computer). It contained thousands of vacuum tubes, was the size of a delivery truck, cost millions of dollars to build and could only do simple math equations. Dozens of burned-out tubes had to be replaced daily, and ENIAC was temperamental. But it was a first. Today, you can spend seven dollars on a calculator that can run rings around ENIAC. A personal computer can do much more.

*Rolling Stone*

**Note:** American English    *favorite, math*
British English    *favourite, maths*

## Exercise 1

Find words from the text which are similar in meaning to the words or phrases below.

1  go up
2  put into
3  entry
4  goes back to the beginning
5  move
6  go towards
7  a small room in which a person shuts himself away to work or relax
8  sit down comfortably and relax
9  hi-fi
10 television programmes which are being repeated
11 take or stop something before it reaches you
12 go darker, go lower
13 something which controls temperature

## Exercise 2

The writer uses four different expressions, all of which mean 'turn on'. Underline them.

## Exercise 3

Tick the most appropriate explanation of these sentences taken from the text.

1  You roll inside.
  ☐ You park inside.
  ☐ You walk inside.
  ☐ You drive slowly in.
2  And since you don't wish to be disturbed . . .
  ☐ You haven't wanted to be interrupted since 6.22 . . .
  ☐ Because you don't want to be interrupted . . .
  ☐ From this time you won't want interruptions . . .
3  The above scenario is no fantasy.
  ☐ This scene is not a dream, it's quite possible.
  ☐ Of course this scene is not true.
  ☐ The scene is a nightmare.
4  You can spend seven dollars on a calculator that can run rings around ENIAC.
  ☐ The calculator will be as good as ENIAC.
  ☐ The calculator won't be quite as good as ENIAC.
  ☐ The calculator will be better than ENIAC.

## Exercise 4

Complete the sentences.

**1** ENIAC contained .............. of vacuum tubes.
**2** ENIAC cost .............. of dollars.
**3** .............. of burned-out tubes had to be replaced daily.

## Exercise 5

Complete the sentences.

**1** When you have closed the door, the security system .............. for the next entry.
**2** When it has finished preparing the meal, the microwave oven .............. itself for the next day.
**3** You can lie in bed and watch .............. of films on TV.

## Exercise 6

Read through the text again. Imagine that you have designed a totally automatic system for your home. Write what happens in the morning from the time ten minutes before your alarm rings to the time that you leave the house.

## Word study

### Ways of expressing 'one'

| | |
|---|---|
| uni- | *uniform, unisex, unique, unit, unite, union* |
| mono- | *monopoly, monorail, monolingual, monochrome, monotonous* |
| one- | *one-way, one-sided, one-time, one-off, one-eyed, one-legged* |
| single- | *single-minded, single-handed, single-parent* |

### Ways of expressing 'same'

| | |
|---|---|
| homo- | *homogeneous, homeopathy, homosexual* |
| sym- | *symbol, symmetry, sympathy, symptom* |
| sim- | *similar, simultaneous, simile* |
| syn- | *synchronize, synonym* |

## Exercise 7

Use the first section of the Word study to find words which are similar in meaning to the words and phrases below.

**1** one kind of clothing for everyone in a job or school
**2** different from everything else of its kind
**3** one type of clothing to suit both sexes
**4** to bring different people together
**5** one company controlling an industry
**6** black and white only
**7** speaking one language
**8** boring
**9** a railway with one track only
**10** having only one eye
**11** with only one side (of the argument) expressed, imbalanced
**12** an object, only one of which has ever been produced
**13** one-direction
**14** in the past but not now
**15** with only one purpose
**16** without help from anyone
**17** person bringing up a child without a marital partner

## Exercise 8

Write in the meaning of the words below. Either guess them or use a dictionary to help you.

**1** uni-cycle.........................
**2** monoplane.....................
**3** monocle.........................
**4** monogamy.....................
**5** monaural.........................
**6** one-track-mind...............
**7** singular...........................
**8** singles bar......................

## Exercise 9

Look at the second section of the Word study. Find words similar in meaning to the phrases below.

**1** a type of medicine which treats illness with something which would cause the same symptoms in a healthy person
**2** a person who is attracted to persons of the same sex
**3** made up of similar things or people
**4** feeling the same as someone, the sharing of their troubles
**5** a change in the body that is a known sign of an illness
**6** a sign, mark or object which represents something else
**7** beauty resulting from regularity of form
**8** happening at the same time
**9** setting watches at the same time
**10** almost the same
**11** a word which is similar in meaning to another word

### Two-word verbs with 'forward'

| ● Literal meaning | ● Transferred meaning |
|---|---|
| *come forward* | *carry forward* |
| *go forward* | *come forward* |
| *run forward* | *look forward (to)* |
| *step forward* | *put forward* |

## Exercise 10

Find two-word verbs in the 'transferred meaning' list that are similar in meaning to the phrases below.

**1** to propose an idea
**2** to move a column of figures or its total into the next column in an accounts book
**3** to anticipate with pleasure
**4** to admit to having done or seen something

# Unit 40

## Language summary

See Student's Book

## Exercise 1

### Holiday Stripes!

Luke Williams of London has an unusual problem. He was on holiday in Palma, and as the weather was hot he decided to sunbathe. Because of the heat, he fell asleep on the beach. He was lying next to a fence, and as a result he was sunburned in stripes! This was because the shadows from the fence were across his body. What's Luke going to do about it? Well, tomorrow he'll sunbathe by the same fence, but he's going to move about 10 cm so that the shadows fall on the tanned bits!

Luke Williams, London.
On holiday, Palma, Majorca.
Weather hot, decided to sunbathe.
Fell asleep next to fence.
Result: sunburnt in stripes.
Reason: shadows from fence.
Remedy: try again tomorrow—
but move about 10 cm!

Read the newspaper story that was written from the journalist's notes above. Then answer the following questions.

1 Why did he decide to sunbathe?
2 Where did he fall asleep?
3 How did he get sunburned in stripes?

## Exercise 2

Look at these notes for other stories. Write out the newspaper reports using the notes. Try and use a variety of patterns from the Language study in the Student's Book.

Mrs Krebbs, Battersea, owns small poodle, 'Pepper'. Went to vet (dog unwell). Dog looked very sick- vet took X-ray, looked at it, and decided to operate. Removed from stomach three spoons, four toy soldiers, eight drawing pins, a brooch, a small bottle of asprins. Mrs K: 'I've been looking for that brooch for two years.'

Kelly Andrews, San Francisco – furious with dentist. Last month had front teeth capped- starting career as a model. Only problem, teeth now pick up radio broadcasts. Opens mouth- music comes out. Says can't go out- too embarrassed. Dentist offered to re-do them. Refused- might get a different radio station that she doesn't like!

Mr Price, Dover. Bought new car. Very annoyed - a noisy rattle whenever he drove it. Took it back to garage three times - couldn't find reason. He got very angry. Said it was worst garage been to. Told garage to get rid of noise or give money back. Garage very worried, so took car to pieces. Didn't find noise. Then looked in boot - two beer bottles rolling around in boot. Noise from bottles. Wrapped bottles up in soft plastic. Noises stopped. Mr Price very happy- until mechanic showed him cause of noise. Said he felt a complete idiot.

## Word study

### Ways of expressing 'two', 'double' and 'both'

| | |
|---|---|
| bi- | *bicycle, binoculars, bigamy, bilateral, bifocals* |
| di- | *dilemma, dichotomy, dialogue, divide* |
| dual | *dual carriageway, dual purpose, dual ownership, dual language* |
| two- | *two-faced, two-piece, two-time, two-seater, two-way switch* |
| double- | *double-bed, double-glazing, double-bass, double-cross, double-check* |
| twin- | *twin-bed, twin-set, twin-headlights* |
| ambi- | *ambiguous, ambidextrous, ambivalent* |
| duo- | *duo, duologue* |
| du- | *duel, duet* |

### Exercise 3

Find the words in the list above which are similar in meaning to the phrases below.

1. a sword or pistol fight between two people
2. two identical single beds
3. a large bed for two people
4. a switch which can be operated from two separate places
5. illegal marriage to two people at the same time
6. spectacles with two types of lens
7. a road with two separate sections, one for each direction
8. a song for two voices
9. a singing group with two people
10. a conversation between two people
11. to cheat someone by going out with someone else
12. insincere, saying one thing to one person and something different to someone else
13. a pedal machine with two wheels
14. having two possible meanings
15. feeling about something in two ways
16. to check very carefully
17. being able to use both hands equally
18. two sets of headlights on a car
19. windows with two sheets of glass with an air gap between
20. a problem with two equally possible but not ideal solutions

## Two-word verbs with 'out'

- **Literal meaning**

  | | |
  |---|---|
  | *get out* | *go out* |

- **Transferred meaning**

  | | |
  |---|---|
  | *hold out* (your hand) | *stick out* |
  | *pull out* | *take out* |
  | *reach out* | *throw out* |
  | *stand out* | |

- **Disappear, make disappear**

  | | |
  |---|---|
  | *die out* | *put out* |
  | *fade out* | *rub out* |
  | *go out* | *wear out* |
  | *knock out* | *wipe out* |

- **Happen suddenly**

  | | |
  |---|---|
  | *break out* | *burst out* |

- **Getting/being clearer, louder**

  | | |
  |---|---|
  | *call out* | *speak out* |
  | *copy out* | *work out* |
  | *find out* | *write out* |
  | *shout out* | |

- **Giving**

  | | |
  |---|---|
  | *hand out* | *pay out* |
  | *give out* | *share out* |

### Exercise 4

Now complete the sentences. Be careful to use the correct tense.

1. It was a very serious speech, but when Anna saw the mosquito biting the speaker's nose she had to ............. out laughing.
2. Fighting ............. out again in the border dispute in Northern Mandanga yesterday.
3. This homework's illegible. You'll have to ............. it out neatly for me.
4. If we aren't careful, the elephant will soon ............. out because of hunters seeking its ivory.
5. Hmm. There are five pizzas, and seven people. We'll have to ............. them out between us.
6. Brutus Cray was ............. out in the third round of his boxing match against Rusty Graziano.
7. A fire-engine arrived, and the fire was quickly ............. out.
8. Can I have a light? My cigarette's ............. out.
9. I can't ............. out the answers to these maths problems.
10. Look at these shoes! They're nearly ............. out, and I haven't had them very long.

# Unit 41

## Potter's green-tongued lizard

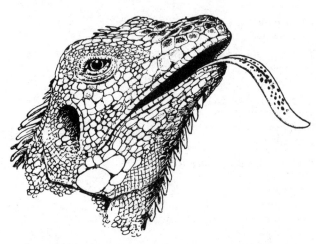

Potter's green-tongued lizard is one of the rarest reptiles in the world. It is only found in one valley in the Owen Stanley Range in Papua New Guinea. It is not particularly unusual, or very different from other lizards in the area, but it is unique and a separate species of lizard.

For centuries it has been killed by the local inhabitants to make necklaces from its skin. This was no threat to the lizard's existence as only small numbers were involved. During the last two decades, cruise ships have been calling at Port Moresby, so that the passengers can visit the remote valleys in the area in order to see a way of life that is totally different. From the early days of the visits, the tourists have bought local handicrafts as souvenirs. The lizard skin necklaces proved especially popular. In order to fulfil the demand for necklaces the local inhabitants began to hunt and kill greater numbers of lizards.

Scientists have been studying the region so that they can classify the many new types of birds, insects and reptiles which are found there. They estimate that the population of Potter's lizards has now reached a dangerous level. They want to ban the hunting of the lizards in order to prevent the lizard's total extinction. They say that Potter's lizard will have disappeared within five years unless something is done at once. They are keen to avoid the lizard's extinction, as they say it is impossible to assess the effect on the ecology of the area. The lizard feeds off insects, which they fear will multiply if the lizard dies out. They say it would be tragic to wipe out a species simply so that tourists can have a cheap souvenir of New Guinea.

A government representative, Mr Joshua Mokobai, puts forward a different point of view. He says that the economy of the region is extremely fragile. The government wishes to preserve the way of life, and to avoid a drift towards the towns and cities. In order to do this, they need to maintain the inhabitants' customs and habits. He doubts that a ban on hunting would work in practice, as it would be impossible to police. He notes that wolves in Britain and poisonous snakes in Ireland became extinct centuries ago, and wonders if the inhabitants thought that this was a bad thing. He says that Potter's lizard is only of interest to a very small group of scientists, and wants to persuade the inhabitants to use the skins of other lizards as well, so that they will still be able to make a living when Potter's lizard has become extinct, an event which he says is inevitable. After all, he says, a few can easily be preserved in zoos.

## Exercise 1

Answer the questions in full.

1 Where is Potter's lizard found?
2 Why is it killed by the local inhabitants?
3 Why wasn't this a threat to its existence?
4 Why have cruise ships been calling at Port Moresby?
5 Why do tourists wish to visit the remote valleys?
6 Why did the local people begin to kill greater numbers of lizards?
7 Why have scientists been studying the region?
8 Why do the scientists want to ban hunting?
9 Why are they keen to avoid its extinction?
10 What do they say would be tragic?
11 What does the government wish to avoid?
12 Why do they need to maintain the local customs and habits?
13 Why wouldn't a ban on hunting work?
14 What does Mr Mokobai want to persuade the local people to do? Why?
15 How would Mr Mokobai preserve Potter's lizard?

## Exercise 2

Either write out a dialogue between a research scientist and Mr Mokobai or act it out with another student. Discuss the problem. Put their opinions into direct speech.

## Exercise 3

Write a paragraph on what you would do about Potter's lizard.

## Exercise 4

Use the chart below to write a newspaper report. The headline is 'Animal activist badly bitten'.

| Event | Purpose |
| --- | --- |
| Animal Liberation Front activists raided a laboratory. | They wanted to release some dogs. |
| The dogs were being kept there. | Scientists wanted to investigate the effects of smoking. |
| The dogs were being forced to smoke 80 cigarettes a day. | Scientists wanted to find more links between smoking and cancer. |
| Five alsatian dogs were taken away. | ALF activists wanted to publicize cruelty to animals in laboratories. |
| An activist, Bennie Factor, put them in the back of a van. | He intended to drive them to his house. |
| At the house, he opened the van doors. | He wanted to let them out. |
| The alsatians attacked him. | Frightened animals attack to protect themselves. |
| He was taken to hospital. | Doctors needed to stitch up his wounds. |

## Word study

### Prefixes related to numbers

| Number | Prefix | Examples |
|---|---|---|
| three | tri- | *triangle, trio, tricycle, triplicate, tripod, trinity, triple, triplets* |
| | three- | *3D (three-dimensional), three-piece suit, threesome, three-figure number* |
| four | quad- | *quadraphonic, quadruple, quadruplets, quadrangle, quadruplicate* |
| | quart- | *quartet, quarter, quarterly* |
| | tetra- | *tetrahedron* |
| | four- | *foursome, four-stroke engine, four-cylinder engine, four-speed gears, four-wheel drive, four-seater* |
| five | pent- | *pentathlon, pentagon, pentangle, pentameter* |
| | quint- | *quins (quintuplets), quintet, quintuple* |
| | five- | *five-speed gearbox* |
| six | sex- | *sextuplets, sextet, sexagenarian* |
| | hex- | *hexagon* |
| | six- | *six-cylinder car* |
| seven | sept- | *septet, septuagenarian, September* |
| | seven- | *seven-sided* |
| eight | oct- | *octopus, octave, octagon, octet, octagenarian, October* |
| | eight- | *eight-week* |
| nine | non- | *nonagenarian, November* |
| | nine- | *nine-hour* |
| ten | dec- | *decimal, decimate, decimalize, decade, December* |
| | ten- | *ten-day* |
| twelve | duodec- | *duodecimal, dozen* |
| | twelve- | *twelve-man* |
| hundred | cent- | *centipede, century, cent, centurian, centenary, centenarian, centigrade, centimetre, centigram, percentage* |
| thousand | mill- | *millipede, millenium* |
| many | multi- | *multiple, multiply, multiplication, multitude, multi-coloured, multi-purpose, multi-storey car park, multi- national* |
| | poly- | *polygon, polygamy, polytechnic, polyglot* |

**Note:** in the old duodecimal British system, twenty items are called a 'score', twelve dozen are called a 'gross'.

### Exercise 5

Look at the words in the Word study. Write lists of those words which fit the categories below.

1 musical groups................................................................
2 children born at the same time......................................
3 geometrical shapes.........................................................
4 old people of a certain age (e.g. 90–99).......................
5 animals, insects etc........................................................
6 numbers of copies of a document.................................
7 motor cars........................................................................
8 measurements, and systems of measurement..............
9 names of Roman months (NB September *used* to be seventh)...........................................................................
10 music..............................................................................

### Exercise 6

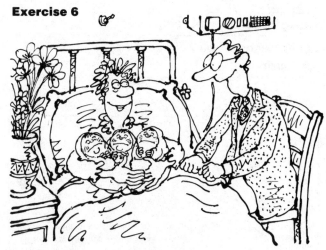

Find the words in the Word study which are similar in meaning to the phrases below.

1 three children resulting from the same pregnancy
2 marriage to several people at the same time
3 a five-sided building
4 a period of ten years
5 a hundred years
6 one hundredth of a dollar
7 an insect with a hundred legs
8 a three-legged camera stand
9 an athletics event with five separate sections
10 to change to a decimal system
11 knowing many languages
12 a very large crowd of people
13 a thousand years
14 a group of three friends
15 a group of four friends

### Exercise 7

knife *knives*

Put the following words into the plural. The first one has been done for you.

1 calf......*calves*......  3 wife................  5 loaf..................
2 half................  4 life..................  6 dwarf..............

### Two-word verbs with 'from', 'into' and 'to'

*do to, go to, hold to, stick to*
*be from, break from, come from, go from, keep from*
*be into, break into, come into, cut into, fall into, get into, go into, lay into, look into, run into, turn into*

### Exercise 8

Now complete the sentences. Be careful to use the correct tense.

1 The intruder ....... into the house through a downstairs window.
2 When her uncle died, she ....... into £200,000
3 Hans ....... from Munich in Germany.
4 The detective is ....... into the robbery.
5 I ....... into a friend I hadn't seen for years.
6 I'm hoping to ....... to university when I finish at school.
7 I made a promise and I intend to ....... to it.
8 I'd only invited a few people, but they invited more, so it ....... into a big party.
9 Mr Mokobai doesn't want the local people to ....... from tradition.
10 The two wrestlers really ....... into each other.

# Unit 42

## Language summary

### Strong language (see Student's Book)
*dare/daren't*

### Exercise 1

---

**dare**            **166**

1  Grammars usually give a lot of information about the verb *dare*. In theory, it can be used in two ways:

a  like a modal auxiliary verb (see 388): third person singular without -s, questions and negatives without *do*, following infinitive without *to*.

> **Dare he tell** *them what he knows?*

b  like an ordinary verb, with -s, *do* and *to*.

> *I shall be surprised if* **he dares to tell** *them what he knows.*
> **Do I dare to ask** *her?*

(*Need* can also be used in these two ways. See 399.)

2  In practice, *dare* is not a very common word in modern English. In an informal style (e g ordinary conversation), we usually use other expressions instead, like *not to be afraid*, or *not to have the courage to*. A sentence like He **dares to say** *what he thinks* is possible, but most people would say **He's not afraid to say** *what he '·nks.*

3  In a few cases, *dare* is still common in an informal style:

a  In British English, the negative *daren't* /deǝnt/ is frequent (modal auxiliary forms: no -s, no *do*, no *to*).

> **I daren't ask** *her – will you do it for me?*
> **She daren't tell** *the boss because she doesn't want to make trouble.*

b  The expression *I dare you to* + infinitive is used by children to challenge each other to do frightening things.

> **I dare you to ride** *your bike through the gate with no hands.*

c  The expressions *You dare!* and *Don't you dare!* are used (for example by mothers) to discourage people from doing things they shouldn't.

> *'Mummy, can I draw a picture on the wall?' –* **'You dare!'**

d  *I dare say* means 'probably' (see 167).

> **I dare say** *it'll rain soon.*

e  We use *How dare you?* as an indignant exclamation.

> **How dare you?** *Take your hands off me at once!*

---

Use the information in the extract from *Practical English Usage* to fill in the missing words in these sentences.

1  Would you ....... to fight a lion?
2  Would you ....... swim near sharks?
3  'You'd better tell her you broke her vase'. 'Oh, no, I .......! She'll be furious.'
4  I heard a noise outside my window last night. I ....... dare ....... look out to see what it was!
5  The little boy said, 'I ....... you ....... jump off that table!'
6  We needn't take sandwiches. I ....... say there'll be a buffet bar on the train.
7  'Sorry, I've opened your letter.' '....... dare .......! It's very private!'
8  'Hey, Dad, I'm going to drink some of your beer!' ....... ....... dare!'
9  I like Miles. He always ....... to give his opinion.
10  '....... you tell your boss what you did?'
11  '....... you ....... to tell your boss what you did?'
12  'I'm going to punch you on the nose!' '....... .......!'

### Exercise 2

In the Student's Book, the Language study lists seven ways of being rude in English.

1  tone of voice           4  sarcasm
2  threats and warnings   5  aggressive expressions
3  familiar terms used to   6  taboo words
    strangers                7  use of social role

Look through the Language study and choose words or phrases to complete the dialogues below. Do not use any taboo words, as it is difficult to use these in a foreign language.

**A**  ....... that's my seat!
**B**  I'm sorry, ....... but you shouldn't have left it, should you?
**A**  ....... ......., I only went to get a drink.
**B**  Bad luck, ....... . You've lost it, haven't you?
**A**  .................................................................
**B**  Oh, yes? Well, ....................................................

**C**  I'm sorry, ....... but can you read?
**D**  Are you trying to be funny, .......?
**C**  Oh, no, ....... . It's just that you've parked right next to a 'No waiting' sign.
**D**  That's quite all right, ....... . I shall only be a moment.
**C**  I'm sorry ......., but ....... a parking ticket.
**D**  ......., ......., I'm a friend of the Chief Constable.
**C**  I don't care if you *are* the Chief Constable, you still can't park here. And it's going to cost you £10.
**D**  .................................... ....................................
**C**  I see. But I just have my job to do, and you're getting a ticket.

## Word study

### Verbs formed by adding '-en' to adjectives or nouns

| | |
|---|---|
| black | *blacken, blackened, blackening* |
| white | *whiten, whitened, whitening* |
| high, height | *heighten, heightened, heightening* |
| strong, strength | *strengthen, strengthened, strengthening* |
| long, length | *lengthen, lengthened, lengthening* |

**Note:** there are a number of these, all meaning 'to make something be like the adjective or noun'.

## Exercise 3

Form verbs from these adjectives.

| | | | |
|---|---|---|---|
| **1** white............................. | | **13** red.............................. |
| **2** bright............................. | | **14** sad.............................. |
| **3** broad............................. | | **15** sick............................. |
| **4** cheap............................. | | **16** short............................. |
| **5** damp............................. | | **17** soft............................. |
| **6** dark............................. | | **18** straight............................. |
| **7** deep............................. | | **19** thick............................. |
| **8** fat............................. | | **20** tough............................. |
| **9** glad............................. | | **21** weak............................. |
| **10** hard............................. | | **22** wide............................. |
| **11** light............................. | | **23** black............................. |
| **12** moist............................. | | **24** quick............................. |

## Exercise 4

Complete the passage.

Tadworth has decided not to build a new by-pass. Instead the existing road will be .............. . Bridges will have to be .............. because of heavy lorries, and the tunnel through Waverly Hill is to be .............. for the same reason. Miller's Lane, which is very bendy, is to be .............. . The town council hope that the time taken to get from North End to Battersby will be .............. by two minutes because of the improvements. Residents are worried about heavier traffic, and are still in favour of the more expensive by-pass.

### Two-word verbs with 'like', 'with' and 'without'

*be like, look like*
*be with, break with, do with, go with, hold with*
*be without, do without, go without*

## Exercise 5

I haven't got an electric coffee maker. I don't really need one, but I'd like one, and it would be useful.
*I could do with an electric coffee maker.*

List six things that you could do with. Then write out the sentences in full.

| | | |
|---|---|---|
| **1** ..................................... | **4** ..................................... |
| **2** ..................................... | **5** ..................................... |
| **3** ..................................... | **6** ..................................... |

## Exercise 6

Imagine a sudden disaster. Many of the essential services are cut off from the place where you live.
*We couldn't do without water, but we could do without TV.*
List five things (1–5) you couldn't do without, and five things (6–10) you could do without.

| | | |
|---|---|---|
| **1** ..................................... | **6** ..................................... |
| **2** ..................................... | **7** ..................................... |
| **3** ..................................... | **8** ..................................... |
| **4** ..................................... | **9** ..................................... |
| **5** ..................................... | **10** ..................................... |

## Exercise 7

Match the people in the photographs below with these jobs:
barman, bus driver, butcher, carpenter, dentist, gardener, model, pilot, policeman, postman.

Then write nine sentences like the one below.
*Number one looks like the butcher.*

1

2

3

4

5

6

7

8

9

10

# Unit 43

## Language summary

**Contrast and comparison** (see Student's Book)

### The Calendar

Very early in Man's history, people began counting time by days, months and seasons, and so had the beginnings of a calendar. There are two types of calendar in use today: solar calendars, which are based on the time the earth takes to revolve around the sun (365 days, 5 hours, 48 minutes and 46 seconds), and lunar calendars based on the time the moon takes to revolve around the Earth. The Western calendar is solar, the Muslim and Jewish calendars are lunar.

The Western calendar goes back to the Egyptians, 23 centuries ago. It was revised by Julius Caesar in 46 B.C., and fixed at 365 days, with a 'leap year' of 366 days every fourth year. This was not quite accurate, because Caesar had introduced too many leap years, and by 1582 the calendar year was about 10 days behind the true solar year. Pope Gregory XIII revised the calendar again, making 4th October 1582 into 14th October. This, the Gregorian Calendar, is the one in use today. Years ending in '00' (1700, 1800, 1900) are not leap years unless they can be divided by 400 (2000). Britain did not adopt the Gregorian calendar until 1752, when New Year's Day was also changed from the end of March to January 1st, and Russia did not adopt it until the revolution of 1917.

But is the Gregorian calendar the best possible way of dividing up the 365¼ day solar year? There have been other suggestions.

### French Revolutionary Calendar

This was in use in the French Empire between 1792 (Year 1) and 1805. Apart from new names for the months, it introduced the ten-day week, one of the attempts at decimalization that failed to catch on!

### The Liberty Calendar

This was an attempt to make the calendar more logical. It was invented by Joseph Barnes in 1917. He proposed a 13-month year, with four-week months. This left New Year's Day as an extra day outside the calendar, and an extra day (as a holiday outside the calendar) every fourth year. Monday would always fall on the 1st, 8th, 15th and 22nd, Tuesday always on the 2nd, 9th, 16th and 23rd and so on. The new month, Liberty, would come after February. Although this was both a simple and logical adaptation of the Gregorian calendar Barnes failed to persuade the US Congress of its superiority.

### Nits-Pyatnik Calendar

This was designed by Moira Nits and Sergei Pyatnik of the Soviet Union in 1984. They say the modern calendar has problems which date back to the Roman Senate, which honoured Julius Caesar and Augustus by giving their months extra days at the expense of February. (July and August.) So, the year divides into 'halves' of 181 and 184 days, and quarters of 90, 91, 92 and 92 days.

Their calendar has 12 months, each of five weeks, each of six days. Tuesday is abolished! This adds up to 360 days, and they suggest a holiday week (five or six days) every year which would be outside the calendar. There would be 15 fewer working days a year, but unfortunately they also suggest lengthening the average working day by 45 minutes.

Rightly, or wrongly there seems to be very little chance of a revision of the calendar, perhaps because it would cause chaos unless adopted everywhere.

## Starting points for calendars

| 1 | Jewish (date of the Creation) | 3761 BC |
|---|---|---|
| 2 | Mayan | 3111 BC |
| 3 | Hindu | 3102 BC |
| 4 | Chinese | 1600 BC |
| 5 | Roman (founding of Rome) | 753 BC |
| 6 | Buddhist (birth of Buddha) | 544 BC |
| 7 | Christian (birth of Christ) | 1 AD |
| 8 | Muslim (flight from Mecca) | 622 AD |

**Jewish years**
13 or 12 months, depending on year.
1980 = 5741

**Muslim years**
354/355 days, 12 months
1980 AD = 1401 AH (After the Hejira)

**Japan**
Dates from the beginning of each Emperor's reign.

## Exercise 1

Write down the following information from the texts.

1 The exact length of the solar year.
2 The date Caesar changed the calendar.
3 What happened on October 10th 1582.
4 Whether 1900 was a leap year or not.
5 The date of the New Year in Britain in 1747.
6 The date Russia adopted the Gregorian calendar.
7 Year 1 of the French Revolutionary Calendar.
8 The number of days in a week in the French Revolutionary Calendar.
9 The number of months in the Liberty calendar.
10 The dates Wednesday would fall on in a Liberty calendar.
11 The number of days in a month in the Liberty calendar.
12 The month named after Julius Caesar.
13 The number of days in the first half of a Gregorian year.
14 The number of days in a Nits-Pyatnik week.
15 The day Nits and Pyatnik decided to get rid of.
16 The number of working days fewer that there would be in Nits' and Pyatnik's year.
17 The date the Mayan calendar began.
18 The Muslim year which is 1980 in the Gregorian calendar.
19 The year Buddha was born.

## Exercise 2

Complete the passage with 'although' or 'in spite of'.

....... it seems unlikely that the calendar will be changed, mathematicians are fascinated by the challenge of designing a new one. ....... work by Barnes, Barwell, Nits, Pyatnik and others, there is little chance of the world dropping the Gregorian calendar, ....... it's failings. ....... Caesar and Pope Gregory didn't design the calendars named after them personally, they are credited with shaping the year as we know it. ....... astronomers and mathematicians did the actual calculations for Julius Caesar and Pope Gregory, their names have been forgotten.

## Exercise 3

Write a paragraph on one of the subjects below.

● Compare the Gregorian calendar with the one used in your country, if it is different.
● Compare the Gregorian calendar and one of the attempted revisions. Say why you think it will/won't be adopted.

## Word study

### Verbs ending in '-ify', '-ize' and '-ise'

-ify *electrify, horrify, identify, justify, simplify*

**Note:** '-ify' means 'to cause or to make', so *electrify* means 'to make something electric'.

-ise/ize *apologize, criticize, organize, sympathize, recognize*

**Note:** these verbs may be spelled with '-ise' or '-ize'. Both are correct. In fact most British newspapers and publishers choose to follow one or the other. *The Times* and Oxford University Press prefer *recognize*, the *Daily Mirror* prefers *recognise*.

-ise *advise, surprise, televise, promise, practise, advertise*

**Note:** these examples must be spelled '-ise', as in these cases '-ise' is not a suffix, but part of the basic word.

### Exercise 4

Match these verbs with the definitions below. Insert the letters in the appropriate boxes.

| | | |
|---|---|---|
| **a** pacify | **d** classify | **g** notify |
| **b** terrify | **e** clarify | **h** unify |
| **c** magnify | **f** amplify | |

- ☐ **1** to make something clear
- ☐ **2** to make someone more peaceful
- ☐ **3** to make someone frightened
- ☐ **4** to make a group united
- ☐ **5** to make something larger
- ☐ **6** to divide something into classifications
- ☐ **7** to make something louder
- ☐ **8** to tell someone about something formally, in writing

### Exercise 5

Match these verbs with the definitions below. Insert the letters in the appropriate boxes.

| | | |
|---|---|---|
| **a** authorize | **e** industrialize | **i** sensationalize |
| **b** colonize | **f** modernize | **j** sterilize |
| **c** economize | **g** publicize | |
| **d** harmonize | **h** romanticize | |

- ☐ **1** to make something modern
- ☐ **2** to give something publicity
- ☐ **3** to make something sterile
- ☐ **4** to exaggerate the romantic side of a story
- ☐ **5** to make something more sensational
- ☐ **6** to try to save money, or use less of something
- ☐ **7** to give someone authority to do something
- ☐ **8** to sing, or move, in harmony
- ☐ **9** to make a place industrial
- ☐ **10** to make somewhere a colony

### Exercise 6

Complete the sentences, using a verb from the list below. Be careful to use the correct form of the verb.

| | | |
|---|---|---|
| advertise | exercise | improvise |
| revise | televise | |

1 He .............. his dog every day.
2 I hate .............. for exams.
3 The BBC are going to .............. the game.
4 I've seen it .............. on television.
5 We haven't got the right tools, we'll have to .............. .

### Two-word verbs with 'after', 'against' and 'for'

| | | |
|---|---|---|
| *call after* | *be against* | *be for* |
| *chase after* | *go against* | *call for* |
| *look after* | *run against* | *fall for* |
| *run after* | *turn against* | *run for* |
| *take after* | *work against* | *work for* |

### Exercise 7

Complete the sentences with the appropriate two-word verb. Be careful to use the correct tense.

1 I'm afraid I ....... ....... the plan. I don't agree with it at all.
2 He ....... ....... a woman half his age, but she didn't want to know him.
3 He ....... ....... his mother. He looks so much like her.
4 Some MPs are ....... ....... new laws to protect tenants from landlords.
5 He's had to ....... ....... his father since an accident two years ago.
6 I ....... ....... ABC Computers plc. I'm their sales representative.
7 He used to be a good friend, but he's ....... ....... me now.
8 In the summer the office windows are open and we have to ....... ....... a background of traffic noise.
9 In the Olympics, Steve Roe ....... ....... Stan Owzat in the thousand metres.
10 Ted's always ....... ....... dreams, without realising he'll never catch them.

# Unit 44

## Language summary

### Quantity

*three/many of which/whom*
*how fast/wide/long? etc.*

### Comparison

*faster/more modern*
*fastest/most modern*

### Punctuation: the question mark

● The question mark replaces a full stop at the end of a sentence asking a question.
*What's the time? How long is it? Have you seen her?*
● It is used after tag questions.
*It's a nice day, isn't it?*
*You wouldn't like it, would you?*
*You went there, didn't you?*
*Hurry up, won't you?*

● It is used after *How do you do?* even though it is only a question in form. (Some people are beginning to drop the question mark in this example.)
● It can be used to show doubt about facts when writing notes.
*Shakespeare, born 1564 (?), died 1616.*
● It comes inside inverted commas.
*He said, 'What do you think you're doing?'*
*'Is this the way?' asked Ken.*

Don't use a question mark after an indirect question.
*I asked her what the time was.*
*I wanted to know if the train went to London.*
*They need to find out where it is.*

---

## Introducing the STREAMLINE AIRWAYS fleet

*'On Stream'* October
Streamline Airways In-Flight Magazine

| Aircraft | Number in service | Passenger capacity | | Typical cruising speed | Length | Wing span | Height | Flight crew |
|---|---|---|---|---|---|---|---|---|
| | | First class | Tourist class | | | | | |
| Boeing 747 | 4 | 42 | 450 | 564 mph 907 km/h | 68.63m | 59.64m | 19.33m | 3 |
| Airbus A-300 | 8 | 40 | 230 | 530 mph 854 km/h | 53.62m | 44.84m | 16.53m | 3 |
| Boeing 757 | 12 | 28 | 150 | 528 mph 850 km/h | 47.32m | 37.95m | 13.56m | 2/3 |
| Boeing 737 | 20 | 8 | 120 | 495 mph 796 km/h | 33.40m | 28.91m | 11.13m | 2 |
| British Aerospace BAE 146 | 6 | — | 82 | 436 mph 702 km/h | 28.56m | 26.34m | 8.61m | 2 |

### Exercise 1

*Their fleet consists of 50 planes, four of which are Boeing 747s.*
*The fleet consists of 50 planes, eight per cent of which are Boeing 747s.*
*The 747 carries 492 people, forty-two of whom sit in first class, and 450 of whom sit in tourist.*
*The 747 carries nearly 500 people, most of whom are in tourist, although about 10% of them are in first class.*

Either practise with another student, making sentences about the other planes, or write one sentence of each type about each of the planes.

### Exercise 2

Either practise with another student or write questions and answers using 'how fast, long, high, wide, many' for each of the planes.

### Exercise 3

Write a paragraph comparing two of the planes. Mention length, height, width, speed, size and number of passengers.

## Exercise 4

Using superlatives, write six sentences about the Boeing 747, and six sentences about the BAE 146.

## Exercise 5

Add question marks or full stops where necessary.

1 Would you mind helping me for a moment
2 He asked how many would be there
3 He said, 'How many will be there'
4 You shouldn't do that, should you
5 I wondered where it had come from
6 John Haskins, 1742–1803 (nobody's sure about the date of death as he died on a desert island)
7 He's always asking questions, isn't he
8 'How do you do' he whispered
9 I've no idea how far it is
10 'How far is it to Bristol' he'd asked

## Word study

### Verbs ending in '-ate'

-ate *accelerate, accommodate, anticipate, assassinate, concentrate, demonstrate, educate, exaggerate, investigate, imitate, legislate, operate, separate, terminate, tolerate*

## Exercise 6

Complete the sentences below with verbs from the Word study. Be careful to put the verb in the correct form.

1 He was ....... by political enemies.
2 The surgeon ....... on him and removed his appendix.
3 I was ....... at Tadworth Comprehensive School.
4 The hotel can ....... up to 220 people.
5 The Porsche ....... and passed the Saab.
6 He wanted to ....... the two rival gangs, but he couldn't, so there was a fight.
7 The concert was even better than I had ........ .
8 The police are ....... the murder.
9 He's a brilliant comedian, he's especially good at ...... famous people.
10 I can't ....... people who are rude to strangers.
11 I found it difficult to ....... on the music.
12 The train ....... at Poole, so you can't go any further.
13 Don't ....... ! It wasn't as bad as that.
14 The government are ....... against drinking and driving.
15 I'll ....... how to do it, so they can actually see how simple it is.

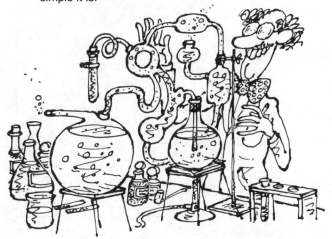

## Exercise 7

Write down the verbs from which these nouns are formed.

1 accommodation............
2 co-operation..................
3 emigration.....................
4 immigration...................
5 fascination....................
6 complication..................
7 irrigation......................
8 irritation.......................
9 toleration.....................
10 radiation.......................
11 education.....................
12 domination...................
13 estimation....................
14 generation....................
15 illumination..................
16 automation...................
17 exaggeration................
18 inflation.......................
19 violation......................
20 contamination..............

### Two-word verbs with 'about'

*be about        go about        see about*
*bring about     hand about      set about*
*come about      look about       stand about*
*get about       put about*

## Exercise 8

Complete the spaces in this text.

Julian Birch has just come out of hospital. His leg is in plaster and he won't be able to ....... about on his own for several weeks. How did this all ....... about? This is Julian's story.

I wasn't doing anything. I was just ....... about my own business. I'd been to a football match. I was wearing a blue scarf, as I'm a City supporter. I noticed a group of United fans in red scarves. They were ....... about near the bus stop, ....... about talking aggressively but not doing anything. I walked over to the bus stop. Suddenly one of them shouted. 'There's a City fan, let's ....... about him!' Before I knew what was happening they all ....... about me. They were ....... about for someone to attack, and I just happened to be the one they chose. I know people have ....... about stories about me being a football hooligan, but I'm not. Anyway, in future I'll be watching matches on TV!'

# Unit 45

**Precautions**

*Don't do it!*
*He told them not to do it.*
*Be careful in case of burns/in case you burn yourself.*

*Be careful to avoid burns/avoid burning yourself.*
*They wear clothes to prevent them from burning themselves.*

---

## 1 DON'T GO ALONE

Whether swimming, canoeing or even fishing, *don't go alone.* Because if trouble occurs, there could be no-one to help.

## 2 IF YOU FALL IN AND CAN'T REACH SAFETY, FLOAT ON YOUR BACK

a. Try to stay calm.
b. Turn over and float on your back.
c. Attract attention by waving *one* arm and shouting for help.

## 3 IF SOMEONE ELSE FALLS IN DON'T GO IN THE WATER AFTER HIM

a. Don't panic.
b. Look for something to help pull him out — stick, rope or clothing.
c. Lie down to prevent yourself from being pulled in.
d. If you cannot reach, throw any floating object — football, plastic bottle — for him to hold on to, *then fetch help.*

### IMPORTANT POINTS TO REMEMBER
### When swimming . . . .

1. Wait at least an hour after meals (otherwise you may vomit and choke).
2. Follow the advice of lifeguards. Don't show off.
3. Don't dive into unknown waters. Always swim in line with the shore.
4. At the seaside find out *when* and *where* it is safe to swim.
5. If you feel tired or cold *get out of the water.* Cold can kill even strong swimmers.
6. Don't wear goggles to dive, except for racing dives.
7. Don't use airbeds or inflatable toys on the water. Wind and tides can quickly sweep them out to sea.

### On the water . . . .

1. Keep equipment in good working order and always wear an approved life-jacket.
2. When boating wear warm clothing and non-slip footwear.
3. Never overload a boat. Only one person should stand at a time. Learn and practise 'Capsize' and 'Man overboard' drills.
4. Stay with capsized boat, you'll be spotted more easily.
5. Tell someone *where* you are going and *when* you'll be back.

### Out and about . . . .

1. Report missing lifesaving equipment (or anyone taking or breaking it).
2. Read and obey notices. Never cover them up.

## ARE YOU AWARE OF THE HAZARDS?

**RIVERBANKS** Keep away from slippery or crumbling banks along streams and rivers.
**CANALS AND LOCKS** Steep sides make it almost impossible to climb out, so keep well away from the edge.
**QUARRIES AND GRAVEL PITS** Deep cold water and hidden hazards make these dangerous places to dive and swim.
**WEIRS** Keep well away. Don't venture where rushing currents can sweep you away.
**PONDS** Cover garden fish ponds and pools with mesh.
**PADDLING POOLS** Toddlers can drown in just a few inches of water. Keep an eye on toddlers near water at all times and always empty paddling pools after use.
**BATHS AT HOME** Keep baths empty and plugs out of reach of small children.
**ICE** Keep off ice covered lakes, ponds or canals.

### THE 999 DRILL

You do not need coins to make an emergency call. The operator will answer a 999 call and ask:

1. Which service you require.
2. Your telephone number.

You ask for the *Police* (or the *Coastguard* if near the coast). The Police or Coastguard will then ask you:

1. What the trouble is.
2. Where it is.
3. Whether anyone is capable of taking action while help is arriving.
4. The telephone number you are speaking from.
5. Your name and address.

By knowing what the questions will be and being able to answer them you will speed the arrival of the emergency services.

---

These extracts come from *The Blue Code for Water Safety* (Royal Life Saving Society, 1982)

## Exercise 1

Imagine that you have just attended a lecture on water safety, where the lecturer summarized all the points in 'The Blue Code'. Write a report on the lecture.
Begin *He said that we shouldn't go swimming alone . . .* or *He told us not to go swimming alone . . .*

## Exercise 2

*If you feel tired you should get out of the water in case you get cramp.*

Read through the advice in 'Important Points to Remember'.

Make sentences with 'in case' and 'in case of'. Think of why each piece of advice is given, and the possible danger it is designed to avoid.

## Exercise 3

*You should avoid wearing goggles when diving.*
Write as many sentences as you can about 'Important Points To Remember' using 'avoid'.

## Exercise 4

Look at the list of hazards. Make one sentence about each hazard using the words below.

| | | |
|---|---|---|
| because | because of | in case |
| in case of | to avoid | |

## Exercise 5

Either practise with another student or write out the dialogue of a 999 call between Herbie and a coastguard. Give all the information mentioned in 'The 999 Drill'.

## Word study

### Prefixes: 'em-' and '-en'

em-  *embitter, embody, empower, employ, emphasize*
en-  *enable, encourage, enlarge, ensure, enjoy*

**Note:** 'em-' and 'en-' mean the same. 'Em-' is used before p and b, 'en-' is used before other letters.

### Prefixes: 'pre-' and 'post-'

| verbs | *pre-arrange, prejudge, pre-pay, predict, precede* |
|---|---|
| nouns | *precaution, prefix, preference, prejudice* |
| adjectives | *premarital, premature, precautionary, prejudicial* |
| verbs | *postpone, postdate* |
| nouns | *postscript* (PS), *post-mortem, postgraduate, p.m. (post meridiem)* |
| adjectives | *posthumous, postdated, postponed* |

## Exercise 6

Match these verbs with the definitions below. Insert the letters in the appropriate boxes.

| | | |
|---|---|---|
| A enliven | C enrich | E enrage |
| B endanger | D entrust | F enlighten |

- [ ] **1** to put in danger
- [ ] **2** to make richer
- [ ] **3** to make angry
- [ ] **4** to put your trust in someone
- [ ] **5** inform, give understanding
- [ ] **6** to make a person or an event lively, more cheerful

## Exercise 7

Replace the words in italics with verbs from the Word study.

**1** The Queen *represents* the power of the state.
**2** I *gave a job to* her.
**3** I *had a very good time at* the party.
**4** He was finding the work difficult, but a few good marks *made* him *feel much better about it.*
**5** They're *making* their house *larger.*
**6** I *gave him the power* to sign letters for me.
**7** We use italics to *make* a word look *more obvious.*
**8** The death of her husband *made* her *very resentful and bitter.*

## Exercise 8

Find words in the second section of the Word study which are similar in meaning to the words and phrases below.

**1** to put a date later than the present day's on a letter or cheque
**2** to arrange in advance
**3** to put off something until later
**4** letters at the beginning of a word which alter its meaning
**5** afternoon
**6** before marriage
**7** after death
**8** a medical examination after death
**9** someone studying for a higher degree such as M.A., M.Phil. or Ph.D.
**10** before its proper time
**11** to judge an issue before knowing the facts
**12** unreasonable feelings about someone or something
**13** to pay in advance
**14** something added to the end of a letter
**15** to go in front of
**16** to say what will happen in the future.

### Two-word verbs with 'across'

| | | |
|---|---|---|
| *come across* | *get across* | *put across* |
| *cut across* | *go across* | *run across* |

## Exercise 9

Rewrite these sentences using two-word verbs with 'across'.

**1** He's a clever politician, he delivers his message very well on TV.
**2** I'm not going by the long route, I'm going to take a shorter route along small country roads.
**3** When I see him on TV, he gives the impression of being a really nice person.
**4** I met an old friend in the street.
**5** I can't communicate what I want to say.

# Unit 46

## Language summary

**Telling a joke or story in the past tense** (see Student's Book)

J.P.L.

### Story 1

The managing director of a small company had been out to see a customer. On his way back to the office he passed a hairdresser's. He glanced in at the window, and saw one of his typists sitting in the hairdresser's chair. He walked into the shop.

'I see you are having your hair cut in working hours,' he said.

'Yes, sir. It grew in working hours,' replied the typist.

'Humph. It didn't all grow in working hours,' he growled.

'No, sir,' said the typist quickly, 'but I'm not having it all cut off!'

### Story 2

A young lady had just checked in to a hotel. Her room was on the fourteenth floor, and as there had been reports about hotel fires in the newspapers, she decided to find the fire exit before going to bed. She looked along the corridor, and saw a door at the end. She opened it and there was a man sitting in the bath.

'Oh! I'm very sorry,' she said. 'I was looking for the fire exit.'

'It's at the other end of the corridor,' he replied.

She started walking along the corridor towards the fire exit, when the bathroom door opened, and the man came out. He was completely naked. She opened the fire door, and ran down the stairs. She could hear the man following her. At last she reached the lobby, the receptionist wasn't there, so she ran out into the street. Suddenly she felt a wet hand on her shoulder. She turned, it was the naked man!

'Where did you say there was a fire?' he asked.

### Story 3

Some scientists were investigating diet and appetite. They were working with rats, which they would train to press a key. When the key was pressed, a drop of liquid food came down a food spout. The experimenters wanted to see if an old, experienced rat could teach a young untrained rat how to get the food. They put a young rat in a cage with an old one, and went away. A few hours later they went to see what was happening. They found the old rat was lying on its back, with its mouth open, under the food spout, while the young rat was pressing the key rapidly with the greatest enthusiasm!

### Story 4

The Town Council at Tadworth wanted to build a new Town Hall. They advertised for builders who could do the job. Three builders applied, an Englishman, an Irishman and a Scotsman. They were asked to come for an interview, where they would give a quotation for the price of the work. The Chief Architect interviewed them. The English builder was first.

'I want a million pounds for the job,' he said.

The Irishman was next. He was asked how much he wanted.

'Two million pounds,' he replied.

He was told that the Englishman had asked for only one million.

'Ah,' he replied, 'But I'll do a much better job, with better quality materials.'

The Scotsman came in last. He was asked for his quotation.

'Three million pounds,' he said.

'What?' said the architect, 'the Englishman wants one million, the Irishman wants two million. Why do you want three million?'

'It's simple,' said the Scotsman, 'there's a million for you, a million for me, and we'll pay the Englishman to do the job.'

## Exercise 1

Read the four stories. If you can, work with another student, choose two jokes each and read them aloud to each other.

Re-tell the stories or write out ones like them using the prompts below.

1 Headmaster/out/see a sick teacher/pass/barber's/ student/chair/hair cut/school time

2 Famous actor/hotel/twelfth floor/fire escape/before dinner/along corridor/door on left/girl in bath/apologize/ try to find fire-escape on right/door opened/girl followed/ actor used to fans chasing him/terrified of bad publicity/ girl naked/ran downstairs/footsteps behind/ran into street/hand on arm/naked girl

3 Researchers/investigate alcohol and effects/use monkeys/teach/pull lever/when lever pulled whisky down pipe/old monkey/teach/young monkey/put both in room/ half an hour/see/had happened/old monkey on back under pipe/young monkey pull lever frantically

4 United Nations decided send rocket Mars/advertisement/ three astronauts/A, B, and C nationalities/asked come for interview/project director/
A $1 million/B $2 million/very dangerous job/big family/ enjoy life first/C $3 million
A $1 million/B $2 million/C million you/million me/send A

## Exercise 2

Think of a joke or story in English. Then write it out, or tell it to a partner.

## Word study

### Nouns: jobs and social roles ending in '-or' '-er' and '-ist'

-or   *doctor, sailor, author, editor, inspector, solicitor, tailor, bachelor, surveyor, professor*

-er   *teacher, driver, writer, lawyer, banker, plumber, grocer, butcher, climber, swimmer*

-ist  *artist, dentist, tourist, cyclist, journalist, economist, violinist, organist, chemist, psychiatrist*

### Exercise 3

Read the text in the Student's Book, Unit 46, 'The Crime of the Century'. List the jobs ending in '-er', '-or' and '-ist'.

### Exercise 4

Read through the jokes and Exercise 1. Add more words with '-er', '-or' and '-ist' to your list.

### Exercise 5

How many of the boxes can you fill? See who can fill the most. Write in the names of famous people who do/did these jobs.

| film director | author |
|---|---|
| singer | footballer |
| painter | sailor/navigator |
| guitarist | swimmer |
| emperor | drummer |
| runner | dancer |

### Exercise 6

Look at the chart you completed in Exercise 5. Either complete it again with your favourite film director, author, singer, etc., or as a class list the names given for each job, vote for the class's favourites, and make a popularity table based on the results.

### Two-word verbs with 'along'

*bring along*   *hurry along*   *send along*
*come along*   *move along*   *take along*
*get along*   *pass along*
*go along*   *run along*

### Exercise 7

Complete the sentences using verbs from the list above.

1  '....... along,' said the conductor, 'We haven't got all day. ....... along the bus, there are people waiting to get on.'
2  When you go to the lecture, don't forget to ....... along a pen and some paper.
3  'Ah, Marilyn,' said the teacher, 'if you see Janice, can you ....... her along to my office?'
4  We've been friends for years. We ....... along together very well.
5  It looks like rain. You'd better ....... along an umbrella.
6  'You're late again,' said the headmaster. 'Now ....... along to your lesson. I'll see you later.'
7  I've heard his plans, and I'm not sure if I ....... along with them.

# Unit 47

## Language summary

### Advice, suggestions and instructions (see Student's Book)

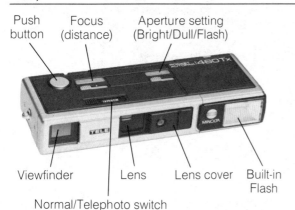

Push button
Focus (distance)
Aperture setting (Bright/Dull/Flash)
Viewfinder
Lens
Lens cover
Built-in Flash
Normal/Telephoto switch

### Taking better pictures

Having a camera is all very well, but you can only make the most of it by knowing how to use it. Here are some of the most common mistakes – and how you can avoid them.

● *Red eye*. This occurs when using flash and makes your subject's eyes look like a good impersonation of Dracula. It's caused by the light from the flashgun bouncing off the retina at the rear of the eye and straight back through the lens.

If this happens with your camera (usually because the flash is close to the lens) then get your subject to look slightly away from the camera.

● *The picture's not sharp*. Hold the camera firmly to stop any movement. Check the focus is correct.

● *Subjects are at the edge of the frame*. Make sure you have them lined up in the viewfinder correctly – particularly if you wear glasses.

● *The subject is very small in the picture*. Don't stand too far away. Most cameras focus as close as one metre.

● *The picture is too dark*. Was there sufficient light? If you used flash, was the subject too far away?

● *The colour's not very good*. This might be due to the processor, but it isn't helped if you're taking a lot of pictures indoors. If the weather's good, take pictures outside in the bright light. Colour films indoors aren't at their best without flash.

● *The baby looks too small*. Again, you should get closer. But there's always a temptation to take pictures looking down at the baby. Try getting down low by lying on the ground; if you're taking pictures of a baby, get a baby's eye view.

● *Subjects look tired and bored*. Taking picture after picture of people in a line gets very boring. So get them to do something. Children will often forget about the camera, and shots of them playing unaware are usually far more satisfying – and interesting.

● *The horizon's not straight*. As well as holding the camera steady make sure it's level.

● *Pictures didn't come out*. Don't give up if you have a few failures. Nobody gets it right first time. Ask yourself what might have gone wrong or, if you have a relative or friend who's keen on photography, ask their advice. Don't forget that even professionals put most of their pictures in the bin.

*Parents* magazine

## Exercise 1

Read the text and find words which mean the following.

1 focussed perfectly, not blurred
2 the person you're taking a picture of
3 the person who develops and prints photographs
4 the line at which the earth and sky seem to meet
5 a place where you throw rubbish
6 become visible (two-word verb)

## Exercise 2

Look at the photographs below. Write advice for the person who took them. Vary the language you use.

## Exercise 3

I was always keen on taking photographs. Whenever I went on holiday I'd take along my camera, and carry it around everywhere with me. Then, of course, I'd bore my friends by passing around the results. 'This is me standing up, and this is my wife sitting down. Actually, you can't see that it's her because she turned around just as I took the photo . . .' Anyway, once I had to go to Athens on business. I had a free afternoon, and it was a lovely sunny day, so I decided to go and look around the Acropolis. It was really strange, because I didn't have my camera with me. I felt naked without it. At first I didn't know what to do. I just stood around watching all the tourists. They were going around in groups taking photographs of everything, and each other standing in front of everything! Then I relaxed, and realized I was free to enjoy myself without the need to run around taking pictures of everything. I could look at things without having to take photographs. I bought a few postcards on the way home, and they're as good a souvenir as anything else. That day freed me from the tyranny of the camera. Now I never take it on holiday. I just use it for family snapshots.

1 Answer the questions.
 *What is the writer's opinion of cameras now?*
 *What do you feel about the writer's opinion?*
 *Do you take a lot of photos? Why?*
 *Why do you prefer your own photos to postcards?*
2 Write a paragraph agreeing or disagreeing with the writer's opinion.

## Word study

### Prefixes: 'dis-' and 'mis-'

These prefixes can be used with verbs e.g. *disagree*, nouns e.g. *disagreement* and adjectives e.g. *disagreeable*. (See Workbook A, Units 6 & 7).
'dis-' carries negative meaning
'mis-' carries the meaning of doing something wrongly or badly

dis- *disappoint, disapprove, disbelieve, discontinue, dislike*

mis- *misbehave, misdirect, mislead, misrepresent, mistake*

## Exercise 4

Match the verbs in Column A with the definitions in Column B. Write the appropriate number in each box.

| | Column A | Column B |
|---|---|---|
| 1 | discolour | ☐ get rid of germs |
| 2 | disallow | ☐ refuse to obey |
| 3 | dissuade | ☐ become the wrong colour |
| 4 | discover | ☐ remove a (telephone) connection |
| 5 | disconnect | ☐ not to trust fully |
| 6 | distrust | ☐ opposite of persuade |
| 7 | disinfect | ☐ lower the price |
| 8 | disobey | ☐ find (for the first time) |
| 9 | dismount | ☐ get off a horse |
| 10 | discount | ☐ judge (a goal, etc.) not acceptable |

## Exercise 5

Find verbs which mean the following. Use a dictionary if necessary.

1 judge wrongly
2 quote wrongly
3 pronounce wrongly
4 spell wrongly
5 understand wrongly
6 read wrongly
7 manage badly
8 inform wrongly
9 calculate wrongly
10 use wrongly

### Two-word verbs with 'around'

| | | |
|---|---|---|
| *carry around* | *look around* | *see around* |
| *get around* | *pass around* | *stand around* |
| *go around* | *run around* | *turn around* |

## Exercise 6

Read the text in Exercise 3 again. Tick any of the verbs in the list above which appear in the text.

## Exercise 7

Write at least six sentences using two-word verbs with 'around'.

# Unit 48

## Exercise 1

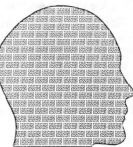

# DO YOU

forget addresses?
miss appointments?
find it difficult to
remember names?

**You can improve your memory by using a few simple techniques.**

*Do you want to know more?*

Write for an introductory leaflet to:
Walter A. Fidel, Coningham Hall,
Ronkem, Wessex WE3 7FA

How good is your memory? Read the list below. Read it *once* only, then close the book and try to rewrite the list from memory. See how many words you can recall in the correct order.

elephant
umbrella
bicycle
mouse
ice-cream
bus stop
whale
lighthouse
dog
piano
chocolate
armchair

If you could only recall a few words and weren't able to remember the order, don't give up. You haven't got a bad memory, you're just not using it correctly.

## Exercise 2

The technique which several 'Improve Your Memory' books use is explained below.
It is supposed to help you not only remember the list, but also to be able to write it in reverse order, or to start and finish at any point you choose.

Read the list again, but instead of trying to remember the words, think of a crazy, silly picture for each word. Then connect each picture to the next one. For instance, picture a huge pink *elephant* holding a yellow *umbrella* in its trunk while it tries to ride a *bicycle*. Suddenly the elephant turns to avoid hitting a giant *mouse* which is eating an *ice cream* as it waits at a *bus stop*. Instead of a bus, a *whale* arrives with a *lighthouse* on its back. The lighthouse keeper is a *dog*, which is playing a *piano*. The piano is made of *chocolate*. The dog's sitting in an *armchair*, which is resting on the back of . . . a pink *elephant*.
Note that the last object, *armchair* is connected with the first, *elephant*, so that your 'mental movie' makes a circle. To recall the list, simply replay your 'mental movie'. To go backwards, just reverse the film, beginning with *armchair*.

## Exercise 3

1  Make up mental movies for the lists below.
2  Try and recall the lists in both directions.
3  Rewind your mental movies and write them out in full. Compare them with other students' mental movies.

| | |
|---|---|
| cat | strawberry |
| typewriter | president |
| boat | book |
| shoe | pub |
| lemonade | aeroplane |
| castle | coffee-pot |
| girl | snake |
| guitar | telephone |
| apple | cassette |
| table | river |
| fish | diamond |
| saucepan | camera |

## Exercise 4

In order to try and remember a telephone number, imagine the number written in huge, red letters on a white wall. This will help you to remember as you dial.
To remember numbers permanently, invent a rhyming system. Think of something which sounds like the number,
one  *bun, fun, gun, sun, nun*
two  *shoe, moo*
Then make up a memory movie using the things you have related to the numbers.
1  Choose one thing to rhyme with each number (1, 2, 3, 4, 5, 6, 7, 8, 9, 0).
2  Make up a mental movie to help you remember the following numbers.
248 23150
679 40753
3  Write one of them down.

## Exercise 5

Keeping a diary is the best way of remembering appointments, but if you have to remember all the appointments for a particular day, go through them in your mind. Imagine yourself greeting people, and attending various meetings. Remember the times by imagining a large clock in each title scene.

1  Write a real diary for next Friday. Write it in note form. Memorize it.
2  On the day, try to remember everything you wrote down. Write a report on what happened. How much could you remember?

## Exercise 6

Some people believe these memory techniques work, others think they are absolute nonsense. You have tried them. How do you feel about them? Write a paragraph giving your opinion.

## Word study

### Prefixes: 're-', 'fore-' and 'co-'

| | | |
|---|---|---|
| re- | (again, a second time) | verbs: *recondition, rewrite, reorganize, redo, recognize, replace*<br>nouns: *return, recount, reflection* |
| fore- | (happening before) | verbs: *foresee, forecast, forewarn, foreshadow*<br>nouns: *forearm, forename, forehead, foreground* |
| co- | (together with) | verbs: *co-operate, coincide, communicate, cohere, coexist*<br>nouns: *coalition, coincidence, co-star, co-writer, co-operative* |

### Exercise 7

Read Exercises 1 to 5 again. Underline all the verbs beginning with 're-'.

### Exercise 8

Write down verbs which mean the following. Use a dictionary if necessary.

1 marry again
2 make yourself feel <u>fresh</u> again (by having a drink or a wash)
3 <u>count</u> something again (or to tell a story again)
4 <u>set</u> a clock again
5 put new <u>stock</u> in a shop
6 <u>style</u> something in a different way
7 <u>join</u> a group you once left
8 <u>issue</u> a book or a stamp for the second time

### Exercise 9

David and Sonya have just bought a flat. The previous owners were very old. A lot of things need doing. The electrical wiring is very old.

*It needs rewiring.*

Continue.
1 The paint's a horrible dirty brown.
2 The paper on the walls is torn and dirty.
3 They left an old sofa. It's nice, but the covers are torn and faded.
4 There's a garage behind the flat, but it's old and falling down.
5 The taps do not work.

### Exercise 10

Match the words in the list of nouns in the Word study with the definitions below.

1 a group of people sharing the ownership of and work for a company
2 first name
3 the part of your face above your eyebrows
4 two political parties working together
5 one of the two major actors in a film
6 a ticket both to and from a place
7 the things in the front of a picture or photo
8 two similar things happening by chance at the same time

### Exercise 11

Fortune-tellers claim and believe that they can foresee the future. People go to them hoping that they will be told about happy events in the future, and that the events will then happen as foretold. Fortune-tellers usually refuse to tell people about bad things, although the most expensive ones do. People want to be forewarned!

1 Mark the words beginning with 'fore-'.
2 Which methods of fortune-telling have you heard of? Make a list.
3 Write a few lines stating your opinion of these methods. Do you belive in fortune-telling?.

### Two-word verbs with 'before'

*come before    put before*
*go before      set before*

### Exercise 12

Answer the following questions as fully as possible.

1 Which letter of the alphabet comes before Q?
2 Which number comes before 44 in the sequence 11, 22, ..., 44, 55?
3 Which number goes before 28 in the sequence 1 3 6 10 15 ... 28?
4 What punctuation marks do you put before the start of direct speech?
5 If the Queen of England came to your house for dinner, what dishes would you set before her?

# Unit 49

## Language summary

### Assumptions and talking about facts
(see Student's Book)

### Punctuation: the hyphen
The hyphen is a small dash used to join double or compound words. Note that a hyphen (-) is half the length of a dash (–) and there is no space between a hyphen and the word it joins. You should leave a space either side of a dash.

| | |
|---|---|
| *well-known* | *fork-lift truck* |
| *out-of-date* | *post-1920s* |
| *pre-war* | *pre-exist* |
| *mother-in-law* | *hard-hearted* |

A good dictionary will tell you when words are hyphenated. You will find that sometimes dictionaries disagree on when a word is one word, and when it is hyphenated.

Some writers would have written the newspaper story below with no hyphens. One rule is to use hyphens in compounds like *co-operate* and *pre-eminent* (where a prefix ends in the same vowel as the first letter of the word).

In England we try not to break words at the end of lines. In writing you should go to the next line and begin the word there. However, nowadays with so many newspapers and documents done on word processors, word breaks and hyphens are becoming more common. When a hyphen is necessary, it should be put between the root and its prefix or suffix. You should never break it in another place.

| | |
|---|---|
| *Ox-ford Uni-versity* | *Eng-lish* |
| *some-time* | *trans-par-ent* |
| *en-gage-ment* | |

---

### A CAREER IN RETAIL MANAGEMENT?

**Smith Wallace PLC** are looking for suitably qualified candidates who wish to train as department store managers. Applicants should hold a good degree and have some retail experience. Preferred age, 25 – 30. Write with c.v. to Ms E. Wright, Personnel Manager, Smith Wallace PLC, Miller Street, London W1A 8WW

Emily Wainwright is the Personnel Manager at Smith-Wallace, a chain of department stores. She has been interviewing candidates for a vacancy as a trainee store manager. It's 4.30 and the last candidate has just walked into her office.

**Emily** Good afternoon, please take a seat. Oh, you've already taken one.

**Rupert** Yes. I hope you don't mind.

**Emily** Not at all. Now, I want to ask you er . . .

**Rupert** Have you got a light? You don't mind if I smoke, do you?

**Emily** Well, .............. I do. I'm a non-smoker myself.

**Rupert** Really? Oh, well.

**Emily** Now, .............. that you went to Oxford University.

**Rupert** Well, yes, but I didn't graduate, ..............

**Emily** Oh, I see.

**Rupert** Yes, .............. they threw me out.

**Emily** .............. you don't want to tell me why.

**Rupert** Not at all. .............. I hadn't done any work.

**Emily** Shall we just go through your application form?

**Rupert** Why not?

**Emily** I see that you're only 22.

**Rupert** Yes, as far as I know. Ha! Ha!

**Emily** .............. you have had some experience with the retail trade.

**Rupert** .............. not really. I mean, I've done plenty of shopping.

**Emily** At Smith-Wallace?

**Rupert** Good gracious, no! I never shop at chain stores. Certainly not the cheaper ones like Smith-Wallace.

**Emily** Well, I don't want to waste too much of your time, Mr, Mr er . . .

**Rupert** Smith. Rupert Smith.

**Emily** Mr Smith, .............. I've been wondering why you want this job.

**Rupert** .............. I don't. It was my father's idea.

**Emily** I understand. Well, I think that's all. Is there anything else that you'd like to mention?

**Rupert** Well, .............. there is. You see my father's Herbert Smith, the owner of Smith-Wallace.

### Exercise 1

Complete the spaces in the dialogue with the phrases below. Some of them may occur more than once.

| | |
|---|---|
| actually | in fact |
| I believe | the fact of the matter is |
| I suppose | as a matter of fact |
| I presume | the fact is |

### Exercise 2

If possible practise reading the dialogue with another student. Write out another interview dialogue. This time the candidate is serious, sensible and well-qualified.

### Exercise 3

Read the story from the *Daily Mail* below.

1 What did Stan hear?
2 What did he assume it was?
3 How many people were working on the dustcart?
4 How much rubbish was the dustcart carrying?
5 What had caused the noise?

*Daily Mail*, Tuesday May 17, 1983

## Hunt for baby in dustcart

A CHILD'S cries from the back of his dustcart stopped driver Stan Anderson in his tracks yesterday. He leaped from his cab and phoned his depot chief.

Mr Anderson and his four crew mates emptied five tons of rubbish into the road at Wexham Close, Luton, Bedfordshire and started scrabbling through it.

Their search ended when Mr Anderson pulled out a brown-haired, blue-eyed, pink-suited doll. The battery-operated voice-box had somehow become activated.

## Exercise 4

There are seven hyphens in the newspaper story. Underline the hyphenated words. How many are needed because a word goes over two lines?

## Exercise 5

Write out these words with a hyphen where you could break these words if you came to the end of a line.

1  question.......................
2  recover...........................
3  outdoors.......................
4  overlook.......................
5  undercover...................
6  laboratory.....................
7  effective.......................
8  development................
9  accountant...................
10  Romanesque...............

11  prescription...................
12  automation...................
13  encouragement.............
14  headmistress................
15  misbehave...................
16  disinfectant...................
17  departure.....................
18  connection...................
19  destination...................
20  direction.......................

## Exercise 6

Put hyphens in these sentences where necessary.

1  He was white haired, middle aged and bad tempered.
2  My great great grandfather came from the United States of America.
3  The new high speed train will replace the out of date diesel electric railway engines now being used by British Rail.
4  His son in law was an undergraduate at Cambridge University in the post war period.
5  'All right,' he said in a high pitched voice, 'I'll co-operate with you. The money is in the bank vault.'

## Word study

### Prefixes: 'out-', 'under-' and 'over-'

| out- | verbs | *outlive, outnumber, outshine, outwit, outmanoeuvre* |
| | nouns | *outlaw, out-patient, outsider, outpost, outdoors* |
| under- | verbs | *under-cook, under-pay, undergo, under emphasize* |
| | nouns | *undercarriage, underwear, underdog, undergrowth* |
| over- | verbs | *over-eat, over-simplify, over-strain, over-produce* |
| | adjectives | *over-ambitious, over-confident, over-emotional* |
| | nouns | *over-anxiety, over-confidence, over-indulgence* |

## Exercise 7

Write the opposites of these words.

1  over-cook.....................
2  over-eat.......................
3  under-estimate.............
4  over-pay.......................
5  underfed.......................
6  under-expose...............

7  over-heat.....................
8  under-charge...............
9  under-ambitious............
10  under-confidence.........
11  over-emphasize...........
12  underload.....................

## Exercise 8

Find words in the list which are similar in meaning to the phrases below.

1  live longer than
2  become more successful than
3  someone who is not part of the group
4  defeat by being more clever than
5  be greater in number than
6  a person who visits a hospital for treatment but who doesn't sleep there

## Exercise 9

Write sentences with five other words beginning 'out-', 'under-' and 'over-'. Use your dictionary to help you.

### Two-word verbs with 'behind'

*be behind*          *go behind*
*drop behind*        *keep behind*
*fall behind*        *put behind*
*get behind*

## Exercise 10

Look at this sentence.
'Oh, dear,' said his teacher, 'I know you've been ill, but I'm afraid you ....... behind in your work.'
Find all the verbs in the list above which could complete this sentence. Be careful to use the correct tense.

## Exercise 11

Now complete the sentences below with the appropriate verbs.

1  When she left prison, the governor said 'You must .............. the past behind you and start a new life.'
2  Nobody liked her, especially her boss. She was always .............. behind his back, and complaining to the managing director.
3  The teacher was furious. 'If no one admits to doing that silly drawing, I'm going to .............. the whole class behind after school for an hour!

# Unit 50

## Language summary

### Type 2 conditionals

| If I had a lot of money, I | 'd<br>would<br>wouldn't<br>would not | stop working. |
|---|---|---|
| I wouldn't stop working, | unless<br>even if<br>if | I were (was) very rich. |

### Punctuation: the exclamation mark

This mark is used to show humour, surprise, astonishment or to give a warning. It replaces a full stop.

*He sat down right on top of the box of eggs!*
*Congratulations, you have won one million pounds!*
*Watch out! There's a car coming!*

**Note:** don't use too many exclamation marks. It makes things tiring to read, and is usually unnecessary.

### Exercise 1

The following statements could be made from the MP's comments below.

*If cigarettes were more expensive, people would stop smoking.*
*People would smoke less, if cigarettes were more expensive.*
*Some people wouldn't stop smoking, even if cigarettes were double the price.*
*People might cut down on smoking if cigarettes cost more.*

Make as many sentences as you can with 'if', 'even if' or 'unless' about each of the other newspaper extracts.

---

#### MPs IN ROW OVER CIGARETTE PRICES

The MP for Cotley said today, 'Cigarette prices should be doubled, then people might stop smoking.' 'Rubbish!' replied an opposition spokesman. 'Price makes no difference.'

---

#### Crime statistics up by 20%

In a statement issued earlier today, the Chief Constable said that more policemen were needed to

---

#### BANK HOLIDAY CHAOS

The five hour traffic jam on the M3 out of London yesterday, prompted the Automobile Association to call for the building of more motorways and to insist that this was now the only solution to

---

#### Stronger penalties

40% of road accidents involve drunken drivers. 'Stronger penalties are required,' says the London Chief of Police.

---

#### England team lose again

England's loss last night (5–0) made it its tenth in succession. Fans are calling for a new manager – and a new team.

---

#### Four million unemployed by next Spring

The head of the Confederation of British Industry today demanded more investment in local industry.

---

#### AIR FARE ANOMALY

A London to Rome ticket costs as much as London to Chicago. The EEC Commission thinks that European air fares are altogether too high and they are now

---

#### 10% of school-leavers can't read or write

The Teachers' Union has been saying for a long time, that smaller classes are necessary if Britain is to improve its educational standards.

---

#### WATER SHORTAGE

The severe drought caused by eight weeks without rain is getting more serious. An official from the Water Board said that every family must make an effort to reduce its water consumption.

---

#### Must build more houses

The latest government report on housing states that there are now 200,000 homeless people in Britain, and that it is essential to build more houses.

---

#### DIVORCE UP

According to figures issued today, the divorce rate has risen by 60% in the last ten years. The Bishop of Southwell commented that people are marrying too young.

## Exercise 2

In Britain, Japan and a few other countries, cars drive on the left-hand side of the road. As they are both islands, there's little need to change.
● Will Britain ever change?
● How many things would have to be changed?
● What would happen on the first day?
● How would such a change be organized?

Make as many sentences as you can with 'if' or 'unless'.

## Exercise 3

A government has a severe energy crisis. They can't afford to import much petroleum, there have been strikes in the coal industry and water power has been reduced by a drought. The Minister of the Interior has decided to draw up a list of ways in which energy could be saved.
*If offices closed earlier, we'd use less electricity.*
Make ten energy saving suggestions, with 'if' or 'unless'.

## Exercise 4

Put exclamation marks where you feel they are needed.

1 Help. Help. I can't swim.
2 She slipped on a banana skin and fell down right into the Queen's lap.
3 Oh, no. It's Superman.
4 Be careful. There's a lot of ice on the path.
5 Well done. You've beaten him. You're the world champion.
6 Liverpool scored in the last ten seconds of the game.
7 Stop. Put your hands in the air.
8 The crowd cheered as I walked off the plane. They were expecting the President, not me.

## Word study

### Prefixes: 'un-' and 'de-'

un-  *undo, uncover, unseat, unearth, unblock*
de-  *depopulate, de-ice, deform, dehydrate, deport*

## Exercise 5

Write the opposite of each verb.

| | | | |
|---|---|---|---|
| 1 | ......... cover | 6 | ......... wrap |
| 2 | ......... dress | 7 | ......... zip |
| 3 | ......... pack | 8 | ......... freeze |
| 4 | ......... lock | 9 | ......... hook |
| 5 | ......... wind | 10 | ......... fasten |

## Exercise 6

Complete the sentences 1–10 with the verbs below. Be careful to use the correct form of the verb.

decapitate    decompose    defuse
dehydrate     de-ice       demoralize
deodorize     depopulate   deport
devalue

1 The guillotine was used to ............. criminals.
2 After the famine, the country was ............. .
3 The soldiers were ............. after their defeat.
4 After playing tennis in the midday sun, she was
   ............. .
5 It was so cold, I had to ............. the doorlocks before I could get in.
6 They were arrested in Mandanga, and ............. to their own country.
7 They used strong-smelling disinfectant to ............. the room.
8 The police found the dead body. It had begun to
   ............. .
9 The soldiers managed to ............. the terrorist bomb.
10 Mandanga has decided to ............. its currency.

### Two-word verbs with 'by'

*call by        pass by*
*come by        put by*
*drop by        stand by*
*get by         stick by*
*go by*

## Exercise 7

Replace the words in italics with two-word verbs from the list above. Some of the two-word verbs can be used more than once. Be careful to use the correct tense.

1 She doesn't earn enough money to *be able to manage*.
2 I don't know how you can *look at the problems* and do nothing!
3 They've got a small sum of money *saved* for their retirement.
4 Her husband was accused of several crimes but she *supported* him.
5 Please, if you're in the area *stop and call at my house* to see me.
6 As time *passes* you forget things from the past.
7 He's very rich. I don't know how he *managed to get* so much money.

# Unit 51

## Language summary

**Writing formal letters** (see Student's Book)

### Exercise 1

Cynthia had ordered a white blouse from The Postal Shop early in November. A blouse arrived in the middle of November, but it was pale green. Cynthia returned it the same day, with a note pointing out the mistake, and asking for a white blouse. She never received the blouse. She received a bill late in December, which she returned. She received this letter today.

The Postal Shop
38 King Edward Road
OXBOURNE
Wessex OB9 2AK

Ms C Whicker
14 Barrow Street
Sandbourne
SB12 8LN

10 January 1986

OUR REF: AC/107

Dear Ms Whicker,

We note that your account of £13.28 has not been paid. With respect, we would like to remind you that our terms, which are stated on our order forms, are for payment within thirty days of receipt of goods. Your account was due to be paid on 30th December. We would be grateful if you could settle your account within seven days. If you have paid recently, please accept our apologies and overlook this letter.

Yours sincerely,

*A. Campbell*

A Campbell (Mrs)
Accounts Dept.

Write Cynthia's reply. Lay it out as a formal letter.

### Exercise 2

Paul Hodges wrote to a hotel in Watermouth, asking about vacancies for himself, his wife and two children, during August. He received the letter below.

SEA VIEW HOTEL
West Cliff Avenue, Watermouth WB15 4EY

Mr P. Hogs
12B Runnymead Court
Magna Lane
Tadworth TD10 5MF

2nd February 1986

Dear Mr Hogs,

Thank-you for your letter of January 25th in which you enquired about vacancies during August. I am sorry to say that we are fully booked for the first half of August. We can offer a double room with shower, and a twin-bedded room (without shower) for the third and fourth weeks of the month. They will be vacant on Saturday 16th. I enclose a brochure which gives more information about the hotel, and a list of our terms. We require a deposit of £10 per head with bookings. Thank you again for your enquiry.

Yours sincerely,

*R. Fawlty*

Randolph Fawlty
(Proprietor)

Write Paul's reply. Point out the misspelling of his name. Say that he would like to book the two rooms for one week, beginning on Sunday 24th. Say that he encloses a cheque for the deposit.

### Exercise 3

Write back to Paul from the hotel. Apologize for the misspelling. Explain that it is a small family hotel, and that during the summer season you can only book the rooms from Saturday to Saturday. Tell Paul that he can of course choose whether to arrive on Saturday or Sunday. Apologize but point out that you have to charge the same weekly rate, and state what it is.

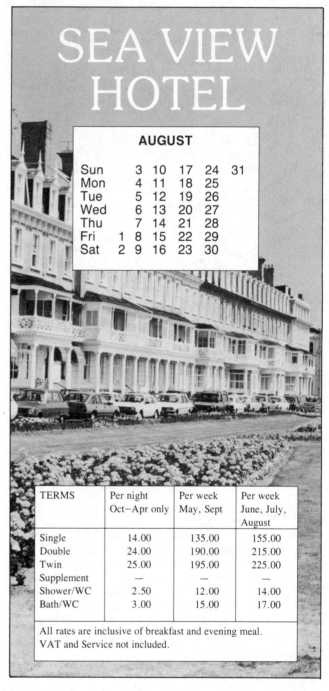

SEA VIEW HOTEL

**AUGUST**

| | | | | | |
|---|---|---|---|---|---|
| Sun | 3 | 10 | 17 | 24 | 31 |
| Mon | 4 | 11 | 18 | 25 | |
| Tue | 5 | 12 | 19 | 26 | |
| Wed | 6 | 13 | 20 | 27 | |
| Thu | 7 | 14 | 21 | 28 | |
| Fri | 1 | 8 | 15 | 22 | 29 |
| Sat | 2 | 9 | 16 | 23 | 30 |

| TERMS | Per night Oct–Apr only | Per week May, Sept | Per week June, July, August |
|---|---|---|---|
| Single | 14.00 | 135.00 | 155.00 |
| Double | 24.00 | 190.00 | 215.00 |
| Twin | 25.00 | 195.00 | 225.00 |
| Supplement | — | — | — |
| Shower/WC | 2.50 | 12.00 | 14.00 |
| Bath/WC | 3.00 | 15.00 | 17.00 |

All rates are inclusive of breakfast and evening meal.
VAT and Service not included.

### Exercise 4

1 If Paul decides to book the holiday, how much will it cost for the family (excluding VAT and service)?
2 If he's paid £10 deposit per head, how much will he have to pay when he gets there?

### Exercise 5

Decide for Paul whether to go to this hotel or not and write Paul's reply.

## Word study

### Prefixes: 'semi-', 'fellow-' and 'ex-'

| | |
|---|---|
| semi- | semi-literate, semi-tropical, semi-skilled |
| fellow- | fellow-citizen, fellow-countryman, fellow-traveller |
| ex- (out of) | extension, ex-directory (telephone number), extrovert, to extradite |
| ex- (past) | ex-president, ex-wife, ex-member |

**Note:** new words can be created with 'semi-', 'fellow-' and 'ex-'.

### Exercise 6

# HAVEN FOR HAS-BEENS?

As your plane flies low over the huge ....... circular bay towards the airport, St Swithin seems like any other ....... tropical island. When you look around at your ....... passengers though, they seem even more well-off than the normal Caribbean tourists. St Swithin, with its zero taxation and liberal immigration laws, has become a haven for the stateless, and for those who dare not go back to their own countries, ....... presidents, ....... kings and ....... ministers from various countries rub shoulders with their ....... political outcasts. Don't bother to look them up in the directory, most of them have ....... directory numbers. They are often afraid of attempts of extradition by their ....... countrymen. In the Coconut Lounge at the island's Grand Hotel, you can see ....... President Gambuko of Mandanga having a quiet drink with ....... King Eric of Ruritania, or another ....... exile. The men that history has forgotten? Well, that is what many of them hope.

Read the newspaper article above, and fill in the spaces with 'semi-', 'fellow-' or 'ex-'.

### Exercise 7

Complete these sentences, using the dictionary extract to help you.

1 'Liverpool beat Arsenal, 3–0, to go through to the .............. where they'll meet Southampton.'
2 'For Sale. .............. house in pleasant neighbourhood.'
3 'The class was sitting in a .............. facing the teacher.'
4 'It's true, I can tell you that. But don't quote me – this is only ..............'
5 'I was .............. for a while before I came round completely.'

---

**semi-** /semɪ/ *prefix* half of; partly; midway: *semi-circle, semi-literate, semi-final.*
ˈsemi·circle, half a circle.
ˌsemi-ˈcircular *adj* (having the shape of a) half a circle.
ˌsemi-ˈcolon (*US* = ˈsemi·colon), the punctuation mark (;) used in writing and printing, between a comma and a full stop in value. ⇨ Appendix 4.
ˌsemi-ˈconscious *adj* partly conscious.
ˌsemi-deˈtached *adj* (of a house) joined to another on one side.
ˌsemi-ˈfinal, match or round before the final (eg in football competitions). Hence, ˌsemi-ˈfinalist *n* [C] player, team, in the semi-finals.
ˌsemi-ofˈficial *adj* (esp of announcements, etc made to newspapers) with the condition that they must not be considered as coming from an official source.
ˌsemi-ˈskilled, having or needing some skill from training but less than skilled: ˌ~-skilled ˈlabour.

### Exercise 8

Read Exercise 6 again. You should be able to find three words where 'ex-' has the meaning 'out of'. Underline them.

### Two-word verbs with 'down' and 'under'

**Literal Meaning**
*fall down, get down, go down, lie down, stay down*

**Transferred meaning**
*bring down, put down, turn down, go under*

**Destroy, put out of order**
*break down, burn down, cut down, knock down, pull down, put down, shut down, tear down*

**Refuse, deny, reject**
*look down on, put down, shout down, turn down (2)*

### Exercise 9

Rewrite these sentences using two-word verbs from the list above.

1 The governor of the prison rejected the prisoner's appeal.
2 The room-maids pulled back the sheets and blankets in every hotel room during the evening meal.
3 He was hit by a bus.
4 She's a terrible snob. She thinks everyone around her is inferior.
5 Business was very bad. Everyone was afraid that the company might cease to be in business.
6 John always said something sarcastic and unpleasant to me.
7 The illness made her feel very depressed.
8 It was a terrible fire. Afterwards the building was destroyed.
9 The worst part of a vet's job is having to kill animals which are very sick.
10 The crowd yelled, booed and hissed the speaker until she was silenced.
11 Talks between the management and unions stopped last night.
12 My car stopped working on the motorway.

# Unit 52

## Language summary

### Reported speech

'I'm tired'.
*He said he was tired.*
*He told me he was tired.*

**Note:** the reported verb usually changes tense. Below is a chart of these changes.

| Direct speech | Reported speech |
|---|---|
| am/is | *was* |
| are | *were* |
| have/has | *had* |
| do/don't | *did/didn't* |
| want | *wanted* |
| did/didn't | *had/hadn't done* |
| wanted/didn't want | *had/hadn't wanted* |
| was/were | *had been* |
| have/has done | *had done* |
| will/won't | *would/wouldn't* |
| shall/shan't | *should/shouldn't* |
| can/can't | *could/couldn't* |
| may | *might* |
| must | *had to* |

### Punctuation: inverted commas and quotation marks

Quotation marks are used to show when someone is actually speaking.

*'What exactly do you want?' he said suspiciously.*
*'Look here,' said Jane. 'You haven't explained it very well.'*

**Note:** double or single quotation marks may be used. For example "*Hello*", or '*Hello*'.

● We use a comma, a question mark or an exclamation mark inside the quotation marks.
*'Hello,' he said. 'What?' she asked.*
*'Hello,' he said. 'Oh no, not you!' she replied.*

● When the reporting verb comes after the statement in quotation marks, you use a comma not a full stop in the quotation.
*'I love you,' he said.*

● Inverted commas are used for things which are quoted, such as extracts from or names of books, plays or films. They are also used with foreign words and words used in an unusual way (for example, humorously or sarcastically). Only do this very occasionally.
*His favourite record is 'Tubular Bells' by Mike Oldfield.*
*The 'plat du jour' is always excellent at that restaurant.*
*It rained every day during the 'summer' holidays.*

● If you need to use inverted commas within a quotation, show the difference as in the examples below.
*He said, "Have you ever read 'Don Quixote' by Cervantes?"*
*The waiter said, 'I can recommend the "Wiener Schnitzel" very highly.'*

**Note:** although we put foreign phrases in inverted commas, it is becoming less common to do so with single words that are frequently used. Kindergarten, café and expresso, are now considered to be English words, for example.

## Exercise 1

Report these sentences.

1 He said, 'I've been so tired recently.'
2 She said, 'I may see you tonight, O.K.?'
3 He said, 'Er ... look ... um ... I can't come tonight.'
4 She said, 'You always seem tired.'
5 He said, 'I'm working very hard at the moment, you see.'
6 She said, 'Oh, come on! I don't believe that. You never work hard.'
7 He said, 'I was at the office until seven o'clock last night.'
8 She said, 'Well, I'll phone you tomorrow.'
9 He said, 'Great. I won't be home till about six.'
10 She said, 'Shall I phone you about half past?'
11 He said, 'Yes. That will be fine.'
12 She said, 'I wanted to ask you something.'
13 He said, 'You can ask me tomorrow, if that's O.K.'
14 She said, 'Right. It can wait till tomorrow.'
15 He said, 'Oh, no. I've just remembered something!'
16 She said, 'Really? I thought you might.'
17 He said, 'Yes, it's your birthday today.'
18 She said, 'Well, you never remember birthdays.'
19 He said, 'Yes, I do. Look I'll see you tonight.'
20 She said, 'Really. You never remember birthdays.'
21 He said, 'I do.'
22 She said, 'You don't. It was my birthday 3 months ago.'

## Exercise 2

VHS
STEREO

**FLAT-SPINNIN'**
The Video
*Featuring*
Terri Persil dancing to
10 great songs!

*Producer*
DAN MIX
*Music*
KLASSIX
*Choreography*
TERRI PERSIL
*Dancers*
FLAT SPIN THEATRE

Imagine that you are a journalist. You have been sent to interview Terri Persil. Terri is a dancer who has starred in two films, *Break Loose*, and *Stepping Out*. She has just released an LP and video which feature her latest dance craze, 'Flat-Spinning'. You have taped Terri talking. Use the tape transcript to write a report on the interview. You should imagine that your readers know little or nothing about Terri Persil.

## Tape Transcript

'O.K. Is that thing switched on? Right, I suppose you know about both the films? You do? Then I won't mention them, O.K.? Look, take a copy of the video, you can watch it later and all the credits are on the cover, if you want to mention the other people involved. Right, I'll begin. I first saw flat-spin dancing when I was on holiday in Puerto Rico. Little kids were dancing it in the streets. They looked really great and I persuaded them to teach me how to dance the flat-spin. It's really difficult. If you make a mistake you can hurt yourself quite badly. Anyway, the dancers are all from Puerto Rico and we made the video on location in San Juan. Dan was superb. He really knows how to make videos. The music's by a British band, Klassix. I'll ... look, the next bit's off the record, O.K.? So don't quote me. They found it really difficult, you see. The drummer wasn't good enough, so we didn't use him on the record. We got a local guy to play drums. Right, you won't mention that, will you? Great, thanks. Anyway the production cost over $400,000, so we'll have to sell a lot of tapes. Oh, maybe you shouldn't quote me on that, either. No, it's all right. You can use that bit if you want, O.K.? We're doing a tour of Europe in May, and a tour of the States and Latin America through June, July and August. It'll be really exhausting. There are ten dancers in the team, even though only six will be dancing on any particular night. You need the extras in case of injuries. I suppose I'm the biggest problem, I just can't get injured. If I am, we'll have to cancel a show, and we'd really hate to let our fans down. Have you got enough? Yeah? Great. Look, have a drink. Oh, and send me a copy of the paper. You will? Thanks.'

### Exercise 3

Put quotation marks and inverted commas into the sentences where necessary.

1. Oh, excuse me, he said, I was trying to choose between the table d'hôte and à la carte. Which would you suggest?
2. Have you seen The Last Tycoon yet? she said. Yes, I replied, but actually I think the book's better than the film.
3. Mandanga has a problem, the minister announced. For the last five years there's been a serious drought – it's hardly rained, even in the wet season.
4. Do you like Paul Simon's records? I asked. Yes, she replied. I love his lyrics. Do you remember that lovely line in his song, American Tune? Which line, I asked. Oh, you know, she said, the line that goes It's so hard to feel bright and bon vivant, so far away from home, so far away from home.

## Word study

### Prefixes: 'anti-' and 'pro-'

Both 'anti-' and 'pro-' can be added to proper nouns and nouns as you choose. 'Anti-' means 'opposed to' or 'against'. 'Pro-' means 'in favour of' or 'in support of'.

anti-  *antiseptic, antibiotic, anticyclone, antifreeze, antidote, antisocial, anti-clockwise*

pro-  *pro-government, pro-Smith, pro-British, pros and cons*

### Exercise 4

Look at the lists above.

1. Find three words which might be used by a doctor.
2. Find one word which might be used in a weather forecast.
3. Find one word which describes something you would put in your car in winter in a cold country.
4. Find one word which describes the direction you would take when turning.
5. Find two words which might be used in a political report.

### Two-word verbs with 'in'

| | | | |
|---|---|---|---|
| *be in* | *draw in* | *hold in* | *put in* |
| *break in* | *fall in* | *keep in* | *run in* |
| *bring in* | *get in* | *let in* | *send in* |
| *call in* | *give in* | *look in* | *take in* |
| *come in* | *go in* | *pull in* | *turn in* |

### Exercise 5

Write two-word verbs which are similar in meaning to the words and phrases below.

1. surrender.......................
2. go to bed.........................
3. burgle.............................
4. enter (2)..........................
5. allow to enter..................
6. earn...................
7. be at home..................
8. make clothes smaller.....
9. tell someone to go in.....
10. visit briefly....................

### Exercise 6

Answer the following questions in full.

1. What do you ask the dressmaker to do with your trousers that are too loose?
2. What kind of person might hold his/her stomach in?
3. What do you do to a new car for the first two thousand kilometres?
4. What do you do with a stiff new pair of shoes?
5. When you are driving and you want to stop on a main road, what do you do?
6. Why do people usually try to keep in with their neighbours?
7. What is another way of saying 'agree with a plan'?
8. Why do ships call in at ports?

# Unit 53

## Language summary

### Type 3 conditionals

*If I had/'d done that, it would/wouldn't have happened.*
*If I hadn't done that, it would/wouldn't have happened.*
*Even if I had/'d/hadn't been there, it would have happened.*
*They wouldn't have done it, unless I had/'d told them to.*

### Exercise 1

## OUTSTANDING SUCCESS

Since the law was introduced for the compulsory wearing of seat belts, the number of serious injuries in car accidents has been reduced by 80%. The transport minister said that the law was an 'outstanding success'.

*If the law hadn't been introduced, the number of injuries wouldn't have fallen.*
*If they hadn't made seat belts compulsory, more people would have been injured.*
*Injuries wouldn't have fallen by 80% unless front seat belts had been made compulsory.*
*If people hadn't been wearing belts, they would have been seriously hurt.*

Make similar sentences about each of the newspaper extracts below.

## TIME-SAVING TERMINAL

With the opening of the new terminal at London's busiest airport, waiting times have been drastically reduced and fewer items of luggage are being lost. 'It works superbly,' says airport official.

## £17.50 BANK HAUL

In a bank hold-up in central London yesterday afternoon, thieves escaped with only £17.50. The bank's safe deposits had been collected by a security van just minutes before.

## NEW CAR

A recently re-designed car has given new independence to 7000 disabled people. It has proved so popular, that production is unable to keep up with the demand.

## RATS JET CRASHES

The private jet belonging to the pop group *The Rats* crashed yesterday killing both the pilot and the co-pilot. *The Rats* themselves were not on board as they had decided to travel by rail.

## HIGH TAX – LOW CONSUMPTION

The recent increase in tax on spirits has cut drinking by 30%, a report out today says.

### Exercise 2

Think about life in prehistoric times. How would things have been different for people?
Make five sentences beginning *If I had been living in . . . .*

### Exercise 3

Think about your life. Make four sentences beginning *If I had . . .* , and four sentences beginning *Unless I had . . . .*

## Word study

| Latin prefix | Basic meaning | Examples |
|---|---|---|
| ante- | before | *antenatal, anteroom, antedate* |
| in-/im- | in, on | *intake, imprint, inflow* |
| in-/im-/il-/ir- | not | *infinite, illicit, immoral, irrelevant* |
| inter- | between | *international, inter-planetary, interchange* |
| mal- | bad, wrong | *malnutrition, maladjusted, maltreat, malpractice* |
| nov- | new | *novel, novelty, nova* |
| pre- | before, in front | *pre-exist, predetermine, prefix, preface* |
| post- | after, behind | *post-war, p.m., post-operative, posthumous* |
| retro- | backwards | *retrospect, retrograde, retrogressive, retro-rocket* |
| super- | above | *superstructure, supernatural, superhuman* |
| trans- | across | *transatlantic, transplant, translate, transform* |

**Note:** some of these have appeared in earlier units. Notice that when we create opposites with 'in', 'im', 'il', 'ir' and 'un' we tend to use 'in', 'im', 'il', 'ir' with Latin words, and 'un' with Germanic words.

## RABID DOG

*A rabid dog has been destroyed, after it was brought into Dover last week. The owner was arrested as she attempted to smuggle her pet off the cross-channel ferry. The vet described her action as 'disgraceful', pointing out that Britain remains one of the few places in the world free of the disease.*

## RUNAWAY LORRY CRASHES INTO SCHOOL

*An out-of-control lorry crashed into a school building and burst into flames, last Sunday afternoon. Fortunately, the school was empty at the time of the accident.*

## SWIM TO SAFETY

A couple had to swim for their lives last Saturday afternoon when their dog was startled by a speed-boat. The dog (a Great Dane) was frightened by the noise and overturned the small rowing boat. All three passengers swam to the safety of the river bank.

## Exercise 4

Find words from the Word study that could be paired with the ones below. The first one has been done for you.

1 *antenatal* clinic
2 ............ idea
3 ............ effort
4 ............ infection
5 ............ travel
6 ............ history
7 a ship's ............
8 a book's ............
9 ............ story
10 motorway ............
11 ............ move
12 heart ............

## Exercise 5

Using the list, add prefixes to these words.

1 ............ date
2 ............ plant
3 ............ rocket
4 ............ existence
5 ............ determined
6 ............ practice
7 ............ formed
8 ............ war
9 ............ adjustment
10 ............ structure
11 ............ finite
12 ............ take

## Exercise 6

Complete the crossword above.

### Across

1 Goes in front of word to change meaning (6)
3 Twice, two (2)
4 More than human (10)
7 Please ....... down. There's plenty of room! (3)
9 Novel, novelty, nova (3)
10 You do this to grass when it grows too long (3)
11 In Latin, 'pre-' (6)
13 Do it again, prefix (2)
14 Across (5)

### Down

1 Something done, or published, or given after death (10)
2 Enemy (3)
3 In Latin, 'retro-' (9)
5 After 1918; after 1945 (7)
6 I wish I hadn't done it in .......spect. (5)
8 'In' can mean 'in' or ' ....... ' (2)
12 You hear with it (3)

## Two-word verbs with 'off'

● **Literal meaning**
*fall off, get off, jump off, step off*
● **Transferred meaning**
*drive off, set off, take off*
● **Disappear, disconnect**
*clear off, die off, kill off, switch off, turn off, wear off*

## Exercise 7

Complete the following sentences with two-word verbs from the list above.

1 Flight 703 ....... ....... at 18.15.
2 Butterflies ....... ....... in the cold weather.
3 Could you ....... ....... the light?
4 Could you ....... ....... the TV?
5 He ....... ....... on holiday with three huge suitcases.
6 'Excuse me, could you tell me when to ....... ....... the bus? I don't know this area.'
7 My garden is infested with ants. I must get something to ....... them ....... .
8 She woke up in the hospital. The anaesthetic had ....... .......
9 '....... .......! and don't come back again!'
10 He ....... ....... quickly, leaving the petrol cap on top of the car roof.

### Solution to Crossword

**Across**
1 Prefix 3 Bi 4 Superhuman 7 Sit 9 New 10 Mow 11 Before 13 Re 14 Trans

**Down**
1 Posthumous 2 Foe 3 Backwards 5 Postwar 6 Retro 8 On 12 Ear

# Unit 54

## Language summary

### Reported questions with 'if', 'whether' and 'wh-'
(see Student's Book)

### Punctuation: the dash

● Dashes are twice as long as hyphens. (dash –/hyphen -).

● A single dash marks a change of idea or sense in a sudden (and a dramatic) way.

*Romeo was waiting for Juliet – but her father came to the window instead.*
*I've seen plenty of TV soap operas – but never one as good as 'Dallas'.*

● Twin dashes are used to show a separated phrase or thought in a sentence.

*Sebastian Coe – perhaps Britain's best athlete – is running in Paris next week.*
*Call me – if you have any time – and I'll explain it all to you.*

● Dashes also separate a list in the middle of a sentence from the beginning and end.

*The group – two guitars, bass, and drums – played for over two hours.*
*I got the shopping – beef, onions, tomatoes and red wine – and took it home to prepare the meal.*

## Exercise 1

Carla has just been for an interview for a job. She's at home telling her parents what she was asked. The interviewer had a check list of questions.
Write a sentence for Carla about each of the questions she was asked. Begin *He asked* ....

---

### Streamline Airways plc
### Heathrow Airport

VACANCIES: TRAINING SCHEME FOR FLIGHT ATTENDANTS

#### Questions: check list

1 Have you ever flown in a plane?
2 Do you like flying?
3 Do you enjoy meeting people?
4 Which school did you go to?
5 When did you leave?
6 How many languages can you speak?
7 What are your qualifications?
8 Were you in any school clubs/societies?
9 Which ones?
10 Do you prefer working indoors or outdoors?
11 Did you study French or Spanish as a main subject?
12 Have you had any experience of first-aid?
13 Are you subject to travel sickness?
14 What jobs have you done?
15 When will you be available to start training?
16 Would you prefer to begin training in January or July?
17 Can you drive?
18 Would you mind living in London?
19 Have you applied to us before?
20 Why do you want this job?

---

## Exercise 2

Alison was interviewed by a market researcher. Read what she says about it below. Then write the questionnaire used by the researcher.

'Do you know something? I ran into one of those market research people in the High Street. He asked me loads of questions about free time. He asked whether I preferred the TV or the radio, and how often I listened to radio. Then he went on about which stations I listened to. He had a list of disc jockeys and asked me if I'd ever heard of them, and what I thought of them – you know, who my favourite was and why. He wanted to know whether I listened to classical music or not, and how often I bought pop records. Then he wanted me to name three records in this week's top ten. Anyway, that wasn't all. Then he asked me if I'd go out with him tonight.'

## Exercise 3

Write ten questions to find out where people do their shopping, when and why. Either write answers to the questions yourself or write down another student's answers.

Write a brief report summarizing the information.

## Exercise 4

Put dashes in these sentences where necessary.

1 We saw most of the animals at the zoo lions, bears elephants and so on but we didn't have time to see the crocodiles.
2 Bob Dylan probably one of the most famous musicians in the world played in Newcastle in 1984.
3 I want you to wash up but be very careful with the wine glasses.
4 Shakespeare, Dickens, Jane Austen, D.H. Lawrence all of them were on our reading list for English literature.
5 Give your homework in if you manage to finish it by Monday morning.

---

# Word study

## More Latin prefixes

| Latin prefix | Basic Meaning | Examples |
| --- | --- | --- |
| ad- | towards, change into, addition | *advance, adapt, adventure, additive, addendum* |
| com- | together with | *combine, combat, commune, combination, communist* |
| contra- | against | *contradict, contravene, contraband, contraceptive* |
| de- | down from, off, from | *depart, debility, declassify, debar, deodorant* |
| e-/ex- | out of | *expel, evict, evolve, extend, extension* |
| sub- | below, under | *submarine, subconscious, sub-contract, subdue, sub-lieutenant* |

## Exercise 5

Write prefixes to complete the words below. Use a dictionary to help you.

1 .......mariner
2 .......diction
3 .......munal
4 .......consciousness
5 .......munism
6 .......pulsion
7 .......diction
8 .......bility
9 .......vention
10 .......ception
11 .......odorize
12 .......contractors
13 .......parture
14 .......bination
15 .......dendum
16 .......band
17 .......aptation
18 .......volution
19 .......bat
20 .......ventures

## Exercise 6

Reorder the letters below to make words from the lists in the Word study.

1 tdtcciaorn .......
2 ccoouussbin .......
3 iioonntabmc .......
4 nvartedue .......
5 snxeteoin .......
6 ledsifaycs .......

## Exercise 7

Replace the words in brackets with words from the lists in the Word study.

1 The warship was sailing into ....... (battle). As it was ....... (going forward), a ....... ( junior officer) shouted, 'Look out, I can see ....... (warships underwater) on the radar.'
2 The empty house was occupied by ....... (a group of people living together). They didn't own the house, and the owners wanted to ....... (get rid of) them. They refused to ....... (make longer) the lease on the house, and said the number of people in the house ....... (broke) the housing laws.
3 I wanted someone to build an ....... (extra room) for my house. He agreed, and I ....... (left) for a holiday while it was being done. Actually I was annoyed to find that the builder hadn't done the job himself. He had ....... (employed) other builders to do it.

## Two-word verbs with 'on'

● **Literal meaning**
*climb on, get on, hang on (1), sit on, stand on*

● **Transferred meaning**
*go on (stage), put on (clothes),*

● **Joining, connection**
*fit on, fix on, screw on, sew on, stick on, switch on, turn on*

● **Continue**
*carry on, come on, drive on, get on (succeed), go on (continue), keep on,*

● **Wait**
*hang on (2), hold on*

## Exercise 8

Complete the sentences with two-word verbs from the list above.

1 You use a screwdriver to ....... something on.
2 You use a needle to ....... something on.
3 You use glue to ....... something on
4 You use a key to ....... an engine on.
5 You might use a nut and bolt, glue, a nail or a screw to ....... something on.
6 You can use a switch, or a control knob, or a tap to ....... something on.

## Exercise 9

Tessa has just stopped her car to ask for directions. Complete the sentences.

Where to? The High Street? ....... on, let me think. Yes, you'd better ....... on along this road, till you come to a crossroads. Oh, look, I'm going that way myself. ....... on a minute. You can follow my car.'

# Unit 55

## ALBUM REVIEWS
### By Pete Stephens

### Alternate Moods
### *Electronic Movement of the Future*
### *(Innocence)* ★ ★ ★

EMF's second LP provides no surprises. We have more of the same formula – complicated synthesizer sounds, electronic drums, and lots of echo on lead singer Howard James' vocals. The melodies are memorable, and the production excellent – clean and crisp. Although I like James' new romantic style, I enjoyed the instrumental cuts even more. There's so much going on at the same time. 'Talk of summer', the 45 from this album, is already a big hit, and I can see the album climbing the charts.

### Faithless
### *Bud Dolan*
### (Amerigo) ★ ★ ★ ★

The long-awaited new album by singer/songwriter Bud Dolan is here at last, and it shows Dolan in a bitter, angry mood as he attacks the evils of society. Many fans will find it hard to like. It's a powerful record, but not an enjoyable one. Dolan's lyrics are cold and savage. The backing, by some of the world's best session musicians, is superb. Mark Hotspur's guitar can be heard on six of the ten tracks, and Sy Dundee and Bobbie Dickens (on drums and bass) provide a marvellous reggae rhythm. For many fans a new album is a 'must'. I hope they won't be disappointed.

### Swords and Sorcerers
### *Warrior*
### (Polyglot) ★

Heavy-metal rock at its loudest and heaviest. I've never been fond of Warrior's simplistic sound, and after their recent Wembley concert, I was deaf for two days. Most of the songs sound the same to me, a steady beat, screaming guitar solos, and silly lyrics. Their cover version of The Rats' 'Bang your head against the wall' sums up their music.

> Bang your head against the wall
> Bang your head until you fall
> Bang your head till you fall down
> Then keep it banging on the ground.

Nonsense? Yes, and dangerous nonsense too.

### Find the Groove
### *Leo Richard*
### (Detroit) ★ ★ ★ ★

Solo album from the ex-lead vocalist of Soul Sensation. It's beautifully produced, with Richard's cool, jazzy vocals over a subtle and sophisticated disco rhythm. The keyboards, played by producer Quentin Jackson, are superb. There are fewer ballads on this album than on the previous one, and Richard moves through a series of styles with ease and grace. 'Thinking of that night', the first (of several) singles from this album is already racing up the charts. Highly recommended.

---

## Exercise 1

1 List the song titles you can find in the reviews.
2 List the musical instruments mentioned.
3 List the musicians mentioned.
4 Find other words for 'album' and 'single'.
5 Find another word for Top Twenty (or Top Forty).
6 Find a word for loud, simple music in a rock style.
7 Find a word for a song first performed by another group, which is now being performed by someone else.
8 An album might have ten songs or instrumentals on it. Find two words meaning 'one of the ten (or twelve)'.

## Exercise 2

Find the meaning in the reviews of each of the words below.

1 lyric................................
2 backing............................
3 solo.................................
4 style................................
5 melody.............................
6 hit....................................
7 ballad..............................
8 vocalist...........................

## Exercise 3

List the instruments you might expect to find in the following musical groups.

1 a heavy-metal group.........................................................
2 a jazz group.....................................................................
3 a classical orchestra.......................................................
4 an electronic group..........................................................

## Exercise 4

1 Which album does Stephens like best, do you think?
2 Which album sounds most interesting to you? Why?
3 Write a paragraph stating what kind of music you like and why.

## Exercise 5

Write out the words of a British or American song that you like.

## Exercise 6

Write one of the following essays:

● a magazine review of two records that you particularly like.
● a magazine article on your favourite group or musician.

## Word study

### Compound adjectives with '-ing'

| | |
|---|---|
| *tear-jerking* | *ear-splitting* |
| *fast-moving* | *long-suffering* |
| *time-saving* | *time-consuming* |
| *earth-shattering* | *world-shaking* |

### Non-standard forms of English

Rock songs try to show the sounds of spoken English. Here is a brief introductory list of other words in non-standard or regional forms of English.

### Scottish

*wee*  small
*bairn*  child
*bonny*  pretty
*aye*  yes
*laddie*  boy
*lassie*  girl
*kirk*  church
*dram*  small glass of spirits (usually whisky)
*slainte*  'Good health!'

### Australian

*cobber*  friend
*tube*  can of beer
*outback*, *bush*  country.

### Small children

*bye-byes*  bed
*choo-choo*  train
*doggy, horsy, pussy*, etc.  dog, horse, cat, etc.

### Northern English

*thee, thy, thyself*  you, your, yourself

### Irish

*I'm after doing*  I'm going to do
*sure*  of course
*poteen*  illegally made whiskey

**Note:** write down any other regional words or expressions you come across.

## Exercise 7

Find words from the Word study that could be used to describe the following.

1 a person who patiently puts up with many problems
2 a job that takes a long time
3 a sports car
4 a very sentimental film
5 a loud rock group
6 an idea which will save a lot of time
7 an event of major importance in the news (2)

### Two-word verbs with 'over'

● **Literal meaning**
*climb over, fly over, get over, go over*

● **Transferred meaning**
*bring over, carry over, hold over* (all meaning postpone),
*be left over, take over*

● **Thinking, reviewing**
*go over, look over, talk over, think over*

## Exercise 8

Replace the words in brackets with two-word verbs from the list above. Use the correct tense.

1 He ......... ......... the fence. (climb up one side and down the other)
2 I'd like to ......... ......... your suggestion. (have time to consider)
3 Continental Computers have ......... ......... SBA Computers Ltd. (buy)
4 ......... all the figures ......... to the next column. (move on)
5 I think we'll ......... ......... the plan until the next meeting. (wait to discuss)
6 I'd like to ......... ......... your idea. (discuss)
7 There's a lot of salad ......... ......... if you feel like some more. (be remaining)
8 The house ......... ......... the river. (have a view of)

The family were called the Meldrums and lived in Sunbeam Avenue. Mr Meldrum was a plumber. He and Mrs Meldrum had produced three children, all boys: in descending order of age they were Gary, Neil and Craig. There was also an Alsatian dog called Ruth, whom I will get to in a minute. All six of them lived in a house not much bigger than ours. Mr Meldrum wore a blue working singlet at all times. He was regarded in the district as something of a gypsy. In fact he was simply the most original man for miles. He made hardly any money but there was more going on in his house than in anybody else's. He had turned all the boys into good swimmers. Gary was exceptionally good and got his picture in the papers for swimming a mile at the age of ten. Neil was a bit of a black sheep and Craig was simply dense, but even they were encouraged in their interests. Neil was mad about stamps and Craig was held by Mr Meldrum to be a promising biologist. In fact Craig's biological studies consisted mainly of picking up privet grubs and eating them. He would also tuck into the occasional centipede. Mrs Meldrum's understandable hysteria at such moments would be overwhelmed by Mr Meldrum's gusto. He was the first man I ever met who had that. In short, he was a ready-made father figure.

The Meldrums taught me to swim. Mr Meldrum, Gary and Neil took me down to the creek in the park. Reeds lined the banks and willows kissed the surface. The water was as brown as oxtail soup but Mr Meldrum said that any water was clean if you could catch healthy fish in it. All the Meldrums could swim across the creek underwater. To me it seemed a fabulous distance. Gary showed me how to hold my breath and keep my eyes open underwater. I could see his hair floating. Inside an hour I was dog-paddling. Mr Meldrum threw his own boys up in the air to turn back somersaults. Then I rode on Gary's shoulder's, Neil rode on his father's, and we had battles in the shallow water.

That was just the start. I think I was eight years old, or perhaps nine. Over the next few years I spent more and more time at the Meldrums'. I would bolt my dinner and scoot around to their place in time to join them for a second dessert. Thus I laid the foundation of my uncanny ability to inhale a meal instead of eating it.

Clive James was born in Sydney, Australia in 1939. He now lives in England, and is a writer and television critic. This extract is taken from his autobiography, *Unreliable Memoirs*.

## Exercise 1

Find words in the text similar in meaning to the words and phrases below. Use a dictionary if necessary.

1 stupid
2 a kind of vest without sleeves
3 the larva of an insect, which lives in hedges
4 an insect with a large number of legs
5 tall, thin, grass-like plants that grow in wet places
6 a small river
7 trees with long branches hanging down to the ground
8 swimming like a dog
9 stop breathing for a short time
10 a movement where the feet go over the head before returning to a normal position
11 run quickly
12 not deep

## Exercise 2

1 Find two words which James uses to mean 'eat'.
2 Which son was the oldest?
3 Which son was the youngest?

## Exercise 3

Tick the most appropriate explanation of these sentences from the story.

1 'He was regarded in the district as something of a gypsy.'
   A ☐ people thought he was actually a gypsy.
   B ☐ people thought he looked like a gypsy.
   C ☐ people thought he moved casually from job to job, and never took a serious interest in one thing.
2 'He turned all the boys into good swimmers.'
   A ☐ he had pushed all the boys into large pools.
   B ☐ because of his teaching, they could all swim well.
   C ☐ he had taken the boys to good swimmers, who had taught them to swim.
3 'Neil was a bit of a black sheep.'
   A ☐ he was different from the others, and a fairly worthless person.
   B ☐ he was shy and timid.
   C ☐ he had black skin and short curly hair.
4 'Neil was mad about stamps.'
   A ☐ he was careless and silly with his stamp collection.
   B ☐ when he was angry, he would stamp his feet.
   C ☐ he was keen on collecting stamps.
5 'Craig was held by Mr Meldrum to be a promising biologist.'
   A ☐ Mr Meldrum spent a lot of time showing him plants and animals.
   B ☐ Mr Meldrum thought Craig's interests and abilities might make him a good biologist one day.
   C ☐ Mr Meldrum made Craig promise to study biology one day.
6 'Mrs Meldrum's understandable hysteria at such times would be overwhelmed by Mr Meldrum's gusto.'
   A ☐ naturally, she would panic, but her panic was destroyed by Mr Meldrum's obvious sense of humour and enjoyment of life.
   B ☐ naturally, she would panic, but he would panic more than her, and then get angry.
   C ☐ naturally, she would panic, but her panic would get worse when Mr Meldrum would eat one too, with great appetite.

**7** 'Thus I laid the foundation for my uncanny ability to inhale a meal instead of eating it.'

**A** ☐ in this way he began the habit of smelling food, but not actually eating it.

**B** ☐ in this way he learned to blow on his meal so hard that it became cold enough to eat quickly.

**C** ☐ in this way he learned to eat so quickly that he could swallow food the way most people breathe.

## Exercise 4

**1** Write a description of someone you knew when you were a child.

**2** Write a short paragraph about something that happened when you were a child that you can remember clearly.

## Word study

### Prefixes from Greek words

| Greek prefix | Basic meaning | Examples |
|---|---|---|
| chrono- | of time | *chronology, chronometer, synchronize* |
| electro- | of electricity | *electric, electrician, electrify, electrocute* |
| hydro- | of water | *dehydrated, hydrant, hydro-electric* |
| micro- | small | *microfilm, microscope, microwave* |
| neo- | new | *neo-classical, neologism* |
| ortho- | correct, standard | *orthodox, orthography, orthopaedic* |
| phono- | of sound | *phonetics, phonogram, phonology* |
| photo- | of light | *photocopy, photogenic, photograph* |
| physio- | of body | *physiology, physiotherapy, physique* |
| psycho- | of mind | *psychiatrist, psychic, psychology* |
| pseudo- | false | *pseud, pseudo-, pseudonym* |
| proto- | first, original | *protocol, protoplasm, prototype* |
| tele- | linking across distances | *telegram, telephone, telescope, television* |
| techno- | applied science | *technique, technocrat, technology* |
| sym-/syn- | sharing with | *sympathetic, sympathy, synchronize* |

## Exercise 5

List the words in your language which are the same (or nearly the same) as one of the words in the lists above.

## Exercise 6

**1** Underline the adjectives in the Word study.

**2** Put a ring around the verbs in the Word study.

**3** Note the remainder. They are nouns.

## Exercise 7

Look at the Word study again.

**1** Tick all the items which would frequently be found in homes.

**2** Put a cross by all the items connected with medicine and hospitals.

**3** Use a dictionary to check the meaning of the other words.

### Two-word verbs with 'round'

- **Literal meaning**
  *come round, gather round, stand round, turn round*
- **Transferred meaning**
  *go round, hand round, look round, pass round*
- **Visit**
  *call round, come round, drop round, go round, pop round*
- **Persuade**
  *bring round, get round, talk round*
- **Wake up**
  *bring round, come round*

## Exercise 8

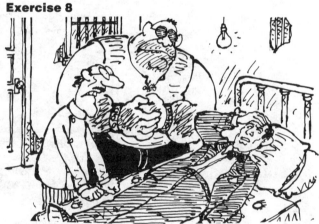

Complete the passage with the correct form of the verb, using the list above.

Dr Nada walked into the room. 'Is he awake yet?' he said. Bull looked up, 'Not yet, boss. I'm trying to ....... him round.' Nada slapped 006 hard across the face. 006 moved slightly. 'He's ....... round now,' he said. 006 opened his eyes. 'Ah,' said Nada, 'we need to have a little talk. I hope I can ....... you round to my opinion.' 'Drop dead, Nada,' said 006 calmly. 'I'm sorry to tell you this,' said Nada, 'but unless you co-operate, some of my friends in London are going to ....... round to see Miss Moneypenny. I'm afraid there may be violence unless I can ....... you round to my way of thinking.' 006 stared quietly at Nada, 'Get lost,' he said. 'All right, men, ....... round me,' said Nada. 'I want you to see the famous agent's death. Bull, ....... round the guns. We're going to have a little game.'
Bull ....... round guns to the six or seven guards who were ....... round Nada.
'We're going to kill you very slowly,' said Nada. 'I think not, Nada,' said 006. 'Listen.'
The sound of a helicopter thundered through the room.
'The building's surrounded,' said 006. 'Go to the window and ....... round the gardens.'
Nada ....... round and at that moment 006 leapt to his feet and grabbed Nada.
'All right, lads,' he said, 'the game's over. Throw down your guns, or Nada dies!'

# Unit 57

## Language summary

### Passives and reported passives
(see Student's Book)

### Punctuation: brackets

● Brackets are used to separate additional information from the rest of a sentence. They are stronger than dashes, and less informal in style. In examinations, it is safer to use brackets than dashes.

*The Beatles (John, George, Paul and Ringo) broke up in 1970.*

*Alison (an old school friend) will be at the party.*

● If the words in brackets are part of the sentence a full stop goes outside.

*He's made three films ('Space Diary', 'Revenge of Jod', 'Galactic Empire').*

● If the words in brackets are a complete sentence, put the full stop inside the brackets.

*I'll meet you at ten. (Make sure you're ready.)*

---

## Exercise 1

The following sentences in the passive can be made about the top picture.

*The motorway is being built at the moment.*
*It will have been completed by June.*
*It will be opened by the Queen.*
*It's being built by McEverest & Co.*

Now make as many passive sentences as you can about each of the pictures.

## Exercise 2

Write a report of the information you wrote down in Exercise 1.

The Motorway is being built at the moment.
*They said the motorway was being built at the moment.*

## Exercise 3

```
DO NOT OPEN
For emergencies only
```

*They do not want/wish the door to be opened.*

Now make sentences about the notices below.

```
DO NOT
LEAVE TAPS
RUNNING
```
```
PLEASE LOCK
YOUR DOOR
AT NIGHT
```
```
PLEASE SWITCH
OFF LIGHTS WHEN
YOU LEAVE THE ROOM
```

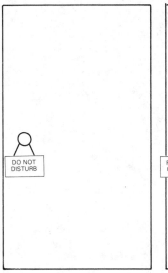

DO NOT
DISTURB

PLEASE MAKE
UP MY ROOM

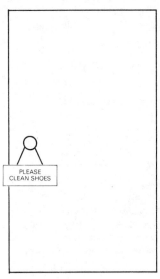

PLEASE
CLEAN SHOES

PLEASE SERVE
BREAKFAST IN
MY ROOM AT
7.00

## Exercise 4

Report these passive sentences.
Begin 'I was told . . .'

1 It will have been mended by now.
2 The sea can be seen from the hotel windows.
3 The letters have been sent.
4 They were posted at 5 o'clock.
5 The work's being done at the moment.
6 It's made locally.
7 It was being done about an hour ago.
8 It will be finished by now.
9 It should not be washed in a machine.
10 They used to be made of cotton, but they aren't any longer.

## Exercise 5

Put brackets in the sentences where necessary.

1 Jenny's got the job but don't tell her that I told you.
2 The M39 from Tadworth to Sandpool is being built now.
3 Fox and Box the estate agents are dealing with the flats.
4 The rings are made of gold. It's mined in Wales.
5 The Rats, Johnny, Vince, Sid and Phil are on TV today.

## Word study

### Plurals: words of foreign origin

Some words can form their plurals according to the rules of the language they come from.

| -ae | Latin | larva *larvae* |
|---|---|---|
| -x | French | bureau *bureaux*, milieu *milieux* |
| -ices | Latin | index *indices* |
| -es | Latin/Greek | basis *bases* |
| -a | Greek | phenomenon *phenomena* |
| -a | Latin | datum *data*,* medium *media** |
| -i | Latin | fungus *fungi* |

**Note:** *these words are now so familiar in the plural that the singular has almost been forgotten and is rarely used. Avoid it by saying *one item of the data*, or *one of the media*.

### Exercise 6

Make these words plural according to the rules given above.

1 cactus
2 plateau
3 nebula
4 crisis
5 chateau
6 appendix
7 alumna
8 axis
9 syllabus
10 bacterium
11 datum
12 bacillus
13 radius
14 thesis
15 addendum
16 analysis

### Two-word verbs with 'through'

● **Literal meaning**
*come through*     *pass through*
*go through*       *see through*

● **Transferred meaning**
*be through*       *look through*
*flick through*    *read through*
*get through*      *see through*

● **On the phone**
*be through*       *put through*
*get through*

● **Survive**
*come through*     *pull through*

### Exercise 7

Complete the spaces with two-word verbs from the list above.

1 A Can you ....... me through to Accounts?
   B Trying to connect you. Hang on, I can't ....... through to Accounts right now. Hold on, they have answered. You ....... through.
   C Accounts. Can I help you?
2 A I hope she can ....... through the operation.
   B It's not a serious operation. Everybody ....... through it all right.
3 A ....... you through with the phone book yet?
   B Hold on, I just want to ....... through and find a number.
4 A Have you ....... through the documents yet?
   B I certainly have, and I can ....... through what they're trying to do.

# Unit 58

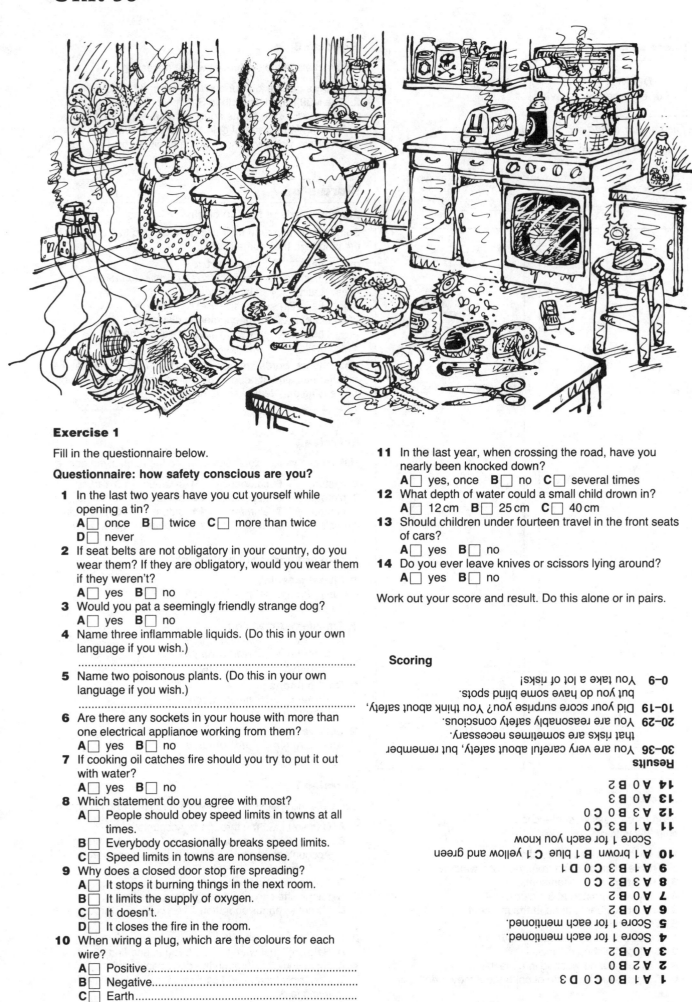

## Exercise 1

Fill in the questionnaire below.

### Questionnaire: how safety conscious are you?

1 In the last two years have you cut yourself while opening a tin?
A☐ once  B☐ twice  C☐ more than twice
D☐ never

2 If seat belts are not obligatory in your country, do you wear them? If they are obligatory, would you wear them if they weren't?
A☐ yes  B☐ no

3 Would you pat a seemingly friendly strange dog?
A☐ yes  B☐ no

4 Name three inflammable liquids. (Do this in your own language if you wish.)
.........................................................................

5 Name two poisonous plants. (Do this in your own language if you wish.)
.........................................................................

6 Are there any sockets in your house with more than one electrical appliance working from them?
A☐ yes  B☐ no

7 If cooking oil catches fire should you try to put it out with water?
A☐ yes  B☐ no

8 Which statement do you agree with most?
A☐ People should obey speed limits in towns at all times.
B☐ Everybody occasionally breaks speed limits.
C☐ Speed limits in towns are nonsense.

9 Why does a closed door stop fire spreading?
A☐ It stops it burning things in the next room.
B☐ It limits the supply of oxygen.
C☐ It doesn't.
D☐ It closes the fire in the room.

10 When wiring a plug, which are the colours for each wire?
A☐ Positive..................................................................
B☐ Negative................................................................
C☐ Earth....................................................................

11 In the last year, when crossing the road, have you nearly been knocked down?
A☐ yes, once  B☐ no  C☐ several times

12 What depth of water could a small child drown in?
A☐ 12 cm  B☐ 25 cm  C☐ 40 cm

13 Should children under fourteen travel in the front seats of cars?
A☐ yes  B☐ no

14 Do you ever leave knives or scissors lying around?
A☐ yes  B☐ no

Work out your score and result. Do this alone or in pairs.

### Scoring

**Results**

**30–36** You are very careful about safety, but remember that risks are sometimes necessary.
**20–29** You are reasonably safety conscious.
**10–19** Did your score surprise you? You think about safety, but you do have some blind spots.
**0–9** You take a lot of risks!

**1** A 1 B 0 C 0 D 3
**2** A 2 B 0
**3** A 0 B 2
**4** Score 1 for each mentioned.
**5** Score 1 for each mentioned.
**6** A 0 B 2
**7** A 0 B 2
**8** A 3 B 2 C 0
**9** A 1 B 3 C 0 D 1
**10** A 1 brown B 1 blue C 1 yellow and green
Score 1 for each you know
**11** A 1 B 3 C 0
**12** A 3 B 0 C 0
**13** A 0 B 3
**14** A 0 B 2

## Exercise 2

*I said I had cut myself several times.*
Report your answers to the questionnaire.
You should write thirteen sentences.

## Exercise 3

Write a paragraph about attitudes towards safety.

---

# Word study

## Constructions with 'first', 'second', 'third' etc.

| | |
|---|---|
| first | *first-aid, first-class, first-hand, first name, first night, first offender, first-rate, first lady* |
| second | *second-hand, second-best, second rate, second sight, second wind, second nature, second thoughts, second childhood* |
| third | *third world, third degree, third party, third rate* |
| fifth, sixth | *fifth column, sixth sense, sixth form* |
| seventh, eleventh | *seventh heaven, at the eleventh hour* |

---

## Exercise 4

Find words in the list above which mean the same as the phrases below.

1 at the last moment, just in time
2 the US President's wife
3 developing countries not in the Western or Soviet blocs
4 brutal treatment
5 not new
6 top quality
7 extreme old age
8 the opening of a play or film
9 someone who has committed one crime
10 traitors, people working with their country's enemy
11 extra-sensory perception (2)
12 extreme happiness
13 reconsidering a decision
14 emergency medical help
15 poor quality
16 automatic, natural, easy
17 what happens to an athlete after being exhausted once, when she/he regains breath
18 not very good (2)

## Two-word verbs with 'up'

● **Literal meaning**
*get up, go up, jump up, pick up, rise up, stand up*

● **Transferred meaning**
*bring up* (children), *come up* (happen), *grow up, wake up*

● **Approach, get closer**
*come up to, drive up to, run up to, walk up to*

● **Increase**
*build up, hurry up, speak up* (louder), *speed up, turn up, warm up*

● **Happen unexpectedly**
*come up, pop up, turn up*

● **Completion, finishing**
*clear up, do up, drink up, eat up, fill up, pack up, save up, shut up, tear up, tidy up, wash up, wrap up*

● **Make up**
See Unit 23

● **Do badly, wrongly**
*foul up, mess up, screw up*

**Note:** there are more combinations with 'up' than any other particle. This is a limited selection.

## Exercise 5

Replace the words in brackets with two-word verbs from the list. Put the verb in the correct tense.

1 My dog always ....... ....... to me when I get home. (greet excitedly)
2 Who's going to ....... .......? (wash the dishes)
3 I'm ....... ....... to buy a radio. (save my money)
4 I can't hear you. Can you ....... .......? (speak louder)
5 She's ....... ........ (put cosmetics on)
6 You've really ....... it ......., haven't you? (make a mess of)
7 I was ....... ....... in Liverpool. (raise and educate)
8 Look, something's ....... ........ I won't be able to get to the meeting. (happen)
9 Can you ....... my dress .......? I can't reach the zip. (fasten)
10 I'll ....... ....... the present. (put in wrapping paper)
11 He ....... the paper ........ (tear into pieces)
12 The petrol tank's empty. Can you ....... it .......? (put petrol in until full)
13 ....... .......! (be quiet)
14 I ....... ....... at 6.30. (awake)
15 I'll help you to ....... ........ (put everything away)

# Unit 59

## Language summary

### Infinitives

*may/could/should/would/might be doing*
*may/could/should/would/might be done*

### Punctuation: the colon

● A colon is used before a list:
*You should have the following items with you:*
*passport, air ticket, money, traveller's cheques.*

● A colon can be used before direct speech:
*The Prime Minister walked to the microphone and said:*
*'I would like to welcome you all here today.'*

● It can be used before examples: (see above!)

● It is used to separate two parts of a sentence where the first part leads you to expect the second part:
*I looked out and saw a wonderful view: I could see the bay, the beach, the cliffs and the hills beyond.*
*He poured my beer on the ground, stamped on my foot and laughed: that's when I decided to hit him!*

● It is sometimes used when writing dialogue:
*John: I love you, Mary.*
*Mary: I love you, too.*
In this case it replaces inverted commas.

## Exercise 1

This is the office at Pettrigrew & Co.
*Mr Pettigrew, the boss, should be there.*
*He should be supervising the office.*
*Actually, he's playing golf. He shouldn't be playing golf, because none of his staff are doing any work!*

Make similar sentences about the people below.

1 Mr Clark, the accounts clerk
2 Miss Davis, the typist
3 Mr Sinclair, the computer operator
4 Mrs Lumley, the filing clerk

## Exercise 2

*Mr Pettigrew would be supervising them, if he were there.*
Make similar sentences about his staff.

## Exercise 3

*Mr Pettigrew, you should be supervising your staff, not playing golf.*
Write similar sentences that Mr Pettigrew says to each of his staff when he gets back to the office.

## Exercise 4

Write down the names of four friends or relatives.
Write a sentence about each of them saying what they may (might) be doing at the moment.

## Exercise 5

Choose one of the problems below. Write a paragraph about it stating what can, could or should be done about it.

- world population
- the energy shortage
- nuclear weapons
- the inequality of the sexes
- pollution
- unemployment

## Exercise 6

Put colons into these sentences where necessary.

1 The new road made our house very noisy the noise of cars, lorries and buses was terrible.
2 The Queen turned and said 'Thank you very much'.
3 I waited and waited for the news. At last it came he was going to be all right.
4 This is what I need a screwdriver, a hammer, some nails and a drill.
5 Hamlet 'To be or not to be.'
  Ophelia 'Sorry? What was the question?'

## Word study

### Prefix: 'self-'

self- *self-assured, self-confident, self-conscious, self-contained, self-defence, self-control, self-employed, self-government, self-respect, self-righteous, self-satisfied, self-sacrificing, self-service, self-sufficient, self-supporting, self-taught*

## Exercise 7

Go through the list.
1 Put a tick by the compounds which could describe someone's personality.
2 List the positive qualities and the negative qualities.

## Exercise 8

Find words which could apply to the following.

1 a newly independent country
2 an apartment with a separate entrance from another apartment in the same house
3 a person who had no formal education
4 a restaurant without waiters
5 judo, karate
6 a person who works alone and is their own boss

## Three-word verbs

| | |
|---|---|
| *back out of* | withdraw from |
| *be up to* | be doing (wrong/or mischief) |
| *carry on with* | continue with |
| *cash in on* | take financial advantage of |
| *catch up on* | bring (work/myself) up to date |
| *check up on* | investigate |
| *come down with* | become ill with |
| *come in for* | suffer from, get |
| *come up against* | meet |
| *cut down on* | reduce consumption of |
| *do away with* | get rid of, stop, delete |
| *face up to* | accept |
| *fall behind with* | fail to (work) quickly enough |
| *get away with* | succeed in doing something bad(ly) |
| *get on with* | be friendly with |

## Exercise 9

Complete the sentences with three-word verbs from the list.

1 I'd better check and see what the kids ....... ....... ......., you know there's always trouble when they're alone.
2 I ....... ....... ....... influenza just before my holiday.
3 Don't let me interrupt you. ....... ....... ....... your work.
4 I hear they're going to ....... ....... ....... the Imperial measurements completely.
5 I'm going to ....... ....... ....... smoking.
6 Jane and I ....... ....... ....... each other very well.
7 You promised you'd help. You can't ....... ....... ....... it now!
8 I've ....... ....... ....... a lot of problems recently.
9 The police have been ....... ....... ....... Withers. They want to know where his money comes from.
10 They reckon he's committed several robberies and so far he's ....... ....... ....... all of them.
11 If they catch him, he'll have to ....... ....... ....... the penalties.
12 I'm so far behind with work. I'll have to work late until I've ....... ....... ....... it.
13 Yes, I've been ....... ....... ....... work, too.
14 It's a wonderful business idea. You'd better ....... ....... ....... it before someone else thinks of it!
15 The government has ....... ....... ....... a lot of criticism recently.

# Unit 60

## Language summary

### Punctuation: the semi-colon

● The semi-colon is not an essential punctuation mark, as it can be replaced by a comma or full stop.

● It is useful, however, as it is halfway between a full stop and a comma. It can be used where full stops would break the flow, while commas would not be strong enough, particularly in lists of examples started with a colon.

*I like to spend weekends relaxing: playing with the children; doing the garden; meeting my friends and neighbours; reading modern novels.*

● It is particularly useful in lists where there are already a lot of commas.
*The plane soon filled up with passengers: tourists with cameras, sun-hats, sun glasses and big smiles; businessmen with calculators, briefcases and portable computers; young people with big rucksacks, phrase books and jeans.*

## Exercise 1

Change commas to semi-colons where necessary.

**1** The village square was always crowded on market day: farmers with sheep, cows, and goats, young children running round looking at the stalls, animals and people, women shopping for fresh eggs, vegetables and dairy produce.

**2** I often think of my schooldays: the hot afternoons trying to concentrate on French verbs, history dates and maps, the cold, wet, winter afternoons on the football field, covered with mud, and the grey, autumn days when time seemed to pass slowly.

## Exercise 2

Write out this text with punctuation marks, paragraphs and capital letters where necessary.

where would you like to go first said our guide as we all walked out of the hotel it was our first visit to london and a city with 8000000 people is very exciting for a boy from the country mr granger spoke first id like to see the tower of london you know with the crown jewels the collection of swords guns and armour the room where the princes were murdered perhaps by king richard III in the 15th century oh no said mrs thomas id really like to see buckingham palace with the guards standing outside they still do stand outside dont they and the queens flag flying over the top if shes at home that is and the balcony where she waves to the people i broke in cant we just go and see the river thames first if weve got time ive been desperate to see the river everybody seemed surprised except our guide who smiled and said dont worry well have a chance to see it all before you go home hurry up the bus is this way

## Word study

### Words which represent sounds

### Exercise 3

Read the story below. Underline the words that represent sounds.

Two mice were sitting in their hole. They were afraid to go out because they'd just heard the cat come into the room. 'Miaow, miaow,' it said softly. Suddenly they heard paws running across the ground.
They listened, 'Woof! Woof! Woof!' they heard.
One mouse turned to the other. 'It's all right, now,' he said. 'The dog's chased it away.'
The mice left their hole, whereupon the cat leapt on them, killed them and ate them.
The cat lay down, purring. 'I always knew it would be useful to learn a second language,' it said.

### Exercise 4

Match the sounds in List A with the animals in List B. Write each number in the appropriate box.

**List A**

| | | | |
|---|---|---|---|
| **1** | moo | **9** | cluck |
| **2** | baa | **10** | quack |
| **3** | woof | **11** | hoot |
| **4** | bray | **12** | cock-a-doodle-doo |
| **5** | miaow | **13** | roar |
| **6** | hiss | **14** | tweet, tweet |
| **7** | oink, oink | **15** | squawk |
| **8** | squeak | **16** | buzz |

**List B**

| | |
|---|---|
| ☐ sheep | ☐ duck |
| ☐ owl | ☐ dog |
| ☐ mouse | ☐ cock |
| ☐ snake | ☐ cat |
| ☐ cow | ☐ pig |
| ☐ lion | ☐ bird |
| ☐ hen | ☐ parrot |
| ☐ bee | ☐ donkey |

### Exercise 5

Match the sounds in List A with the things happening in List B. Write each number in the appropriate box.

**List A**          **List B**

| | | |
|---|---|---|
| **1** | pop | ☐ a door slamming shut |
| **2** | splash | ☐ a champagne bottle opening |
| **3** | bang | ☐ a car horn being pushed |
| **4** | boom | ☐ an alarm ringing |
| **5** | honk, honk | ☐ something falling into water |
| **6** | tick-tock | ☐ a door being knocked |
| **7** | ting-a-ling | ☐ a bell/buzzer being pushed |
| **8** | rat-tat-tat | ☐ a clock ticking |
| **9** | buzz | ☐ an explosion |

## Three-word verbs

| | |
|---|---|
| *go back on* | fail to keep a promise |
| *go in for* | take part in, be interested in |
| *hold out for* | continue a struggle or dispute for |
| *join in with* | participate in |
| *keep out of* | avoid |
| *live up to* | achieve what is expected of oneself |
| *look back on* | think about the past |
| *look down on* | feel superior to |
| *look forward to* | anticipate with pleasure |
| *make up for* | compensate for |
| *put up with* | tolerate |
| *run out of* | have none left |
| *send away for* | write to ask for |
| *walk out on* | leave, desert |
| *write off for* | order (goods) by post |

### Exercise 6

Complete the spaces with three-word verbs from the list above.

1 I can't ....... ....... ....... his rudeness any longer!
2 It's mail order. I ....... ....... ....... it.
3 Give me the address. I'll ....... ....... ....... one, too.
4 He ....... ....... ....... his wife and family.
5 The workers are on strike. They're ....... ....... ....... better conditions.
6 But you promised! You can't ....... ....... ....... your word.
7 I'm ....... ....... ....... my holiday.
8 He's a terrible snob. He ....... ....... ....... everyone.
9 Smith was in prison for 3 years before they found out he was innocent. Nothing can ....... ....... ....... that lost time.
10 Come on! ....... ....... ....... us, we're having a great game of football.
11 No, thanks. I've never ....... ....... ....... football.
12 It's difficult for him to ....... ....... ....... his parents' expectations.
13 Oh, no. I've ....... ....... ....... petrol, and it's miles to a garage.
14 I often ....... ....... ....... my schooldays.
15 Look, try and ....... ....... ....... trouble, if you can!

## Word study and Two-word verbs: Index

| Unit | Word study | Two-word verbs | Unit | Word study | Two-word verbs |
|---|---|---|---|---|---|
| 31 | **Nouns**<br>-ability, -ibility | catch +<br>drop + | 46 | **Nouns**<br>-or, -er, -ist | + along |
| 32 | **Nouns and adjectives**<br>-ist, -ism, -ive | draw +<br>lay + | 47 | **Prefixes**<br>dis-, mis- | + around |
| 33 | **Nouns**<br>-or, -our, -ure | add up – end up | 48 | **Prefixes**<br>re-, fore-, co- | + before |
| 34 | **Nouns**<br>-hood, -dom, -ship | fed up – mix up | 49 | **Prefixes**<br>out-, under-, over- | + behind |
| 35 | **Nouns**<br>-al, -oid | own up – sum up | 50 | **Prefixes**<br>un-, de- | + by |
| 36 | **Nouns**<br>-ian, -ant, -ent | talk over – write off | 51 | **Prefixes**<br>semi-, fellow-, ex- | + down,<br>+ under |
| 37 | **Adjective order** | + away | 52 | **Prefixes**<br>anti-, pro- | + in |
| 38 | **Review of adjectives** | + back | 53 | **Latin prefixes**<br>ante-, in-, im-, il-, ir-,<br>inter-, mal-, nov-,<br>pre-, post-, retro-,<br>super-, trans- | + off |
| 39 | **Ways of expressing 'one'<br>and 'same'**<br>uni-, mono-, one-,<br>single-, homo-, sym-,<br>sim-, syn- | + forward | 54 | **Latin prefixes**<br>ad-, com-, contra-, de-,<br>e-, ex-, sub- | + on |
| 40 | **Ways of expresing 'two',<br>'double' and 'both'**<br>bi-, di-, dual-, two-,<br>double-, twin-, ambi-,<br>duo-, du- | +out | 55 | **Compound adjectives<br>with -ing'<br>Non-standard forms<br>of English** | + over |
| 41 | **Prefixes related to<br>numbers** | + from<br>+ into<br>+ to | 56 | **Greek prefixes**<br>chrono-, electro-,<br>hydro-, micro, neo-, ortho-,<br>phono-, photo-, physio-,<br>psycho-, pseudo-, proto-,<br>tele-, techno-, sym-, syn- | + round |
| 42 | **Verbs formed by adding<br>'en' to adjectives or<br>nouns** | + like<br>+ with<br>+ without | 57 | **Plurals: words of foreign<br>origin** | + through |
| 43 | **Verbs**<br>-ify, -ize, -ise | + after<br>+ against<br>+ for | 58 | **Constructions with 'first-',<br>'second-', 'third-', etc.** | + up (+) |
| 44 | **Verbs**<br>-ate | + about | 59 | **Prefix**<br>self- | three-word verbs |
| 45 | **Prefixes**<br>em-, en-, pre-, post- | + across | 60 | **Words which represent<br>sounds** | three-word verbs |

*Workbook A* has already provided practice in two-word verbs and word building.